CHEMISTRY OF BRAIN METABOLISM
IN HEALTH AND DISEASE

Publication Number 406

AMERICAN LECTURE SERIES®

A Monograph in

The BANNERSTONE DIVISION *of*

AMERICAN LECTURES IN LIVING CHEMISTRY

Edited by

I. NEWTON KUGELMASS, M.D., Ph.D., Sc.,D.

Consultant to the Departments of Health and Hospitals

New York, New York

THE CHEMISTRY OF
BRAIN METABOLISM
IN *HEALTH* AND *DISEASE*

By

J. H. QUASTEL, Ph.D., D.Sc., F.R.S.C., F.R.S.

Professor of Biochemistry
McGill University
Montreal, Canada
and
Director
McGill-Montreal General Hospital Research Institute
Montreal, Canada
Formerly Fellow of Trinity College, Cambridge

and

DAVID M. J. QUASTEL, M.D., C.M.

Physiology Department
McGill University
Montreal, Canada

CHARLES C THOMAS • PUBLISHER
Springfield • Illinois U.S.A.

MIDDLEBURY COLLEGE
LIBRARY

CHARLES C THOMAS • PUBLISHER

BANNERSTONE HOUSE

301-327 East Lawrence Avenue, Springfield, Illinois, U.S.A.

With THOMAS BOOKS careful attention is given to all details of manufacturing and design. It is the Publisher's desire to present books that are satisfactory as to their physical qualities and artistic possibilities and appropriate for their particular use. THOMAS BOOKS will be true to those laws of quality that assure a good name and good will.

Printed in the United States of America

FOREWORD

Our *Living Chemistry Series* was conceived by Editor and Publisher to advance the newer knowledge of chemical medicine in the cause of clinical practice. The interdependence of chemistry and medicine is so great that physicians are turning to chemistry, and chemists to medicine in order to understand the underlying basis of life processes in health and disease. Once chemical truths, proofs and convictions become sound foundations for clinical phenomena, key hybrid investigators clarify the bewildering panorama of biochemical progress for application in everyday practice, stimulation of experimental research and extension of postgraduate instruction. Each of our monographs thus unravels the chemical mechanisms and clinical management of many diseases that have remained relatively static in the minds of medical men for three thousand years. Our new Series is charged with the *nisus élan* of chemical wisdom, supreme in choice of international authors, optimal in standards of chemical scholarship, provocative in imagination for experimental research, comprehensive in discussions of scientific medicine, and authoritative in chemical perspectives of human disorders.

The authors from McGill explore the brain as a chemical system with unique functions, made possible by the chemical transformation of raw materials derived from the blood stream. The dynamic mechanisms of these chemical processes are integrated for the normal brain as a basis for intermediary chemical derangements delineated for the disordered brain. With such lucid exposition of the complex stages of brain metabolism, of the direct interferences with intermediary reactions, and of the diverse disturbances in the regulatory systems, we are now able to understand many phenomena underlying the behavior of nerve, brain and mind in health and disease. Aristotle asked how the mind is attached to the body; Dr. Quastel answers chemically with the freshness of a teacher and vitality of a researcher. The brain has been a black box whose working has been known only by comparing output with input until recent chemical probings of its vital interior. Current concepts of brain metabolism thus constitute the basis for an expanding science of the living brain.

I. Newton Kugelmass, M.D., Ph.D., Sc.D., *Editor*

PREFACE

This book, intended for students of biochemistry and of medicine, for physicians who wish to refresh their memories of underlying chemical mechanisms in brain function, and for those in related fields interested in the subject of neurochemistry, attempts to give a brief survey of the chemical processes that take place in the brain during health and in cerebral disease. The subject of Neurochemistry has now grown so rapidly, merging into so many disciplines — neurophysiology, pharmacology, cytochemistry, psychiatry, endocrinology — that it is not possible to make an adequate survey in a book of these dimensions. We have attempted only to present what seem to us to be some highlights of the subject, but to give sufficient references to enable the reader to pursue his enquiries elsewhere. We refer frequently to the subject matter and discussions in the various neurochemical symposia, which have been prominent in recent years, and to a variety of monographs and other works of reference. This is not a text book of biochemistry or of neurochemistry. It is presupposed that readers of this book have already some acquaintance with elementary biochemistry.

CONTENTS

CHEMISTRY OF BRAIN METABOLISM
IN HEALTH AND DISEASE

ENERGY METABOLISM OF THE BRAIN

INTRODUCTION

THE integrative activity of the central nervous system, whatever the physiological mechanisms by which it is mediated, depends ultimately upon its endogenous energy supply. Disturbances at this level are often implicated in cerebral dysfunction or alteration. Accordingly, first place will be given to consideration of oxygen and carbohydrate metabolism of the brain.

OXYGEN CONSUMPTION BY THE BRAIN *IN VIVO*

It is well known that the brain is highly vulnerable to oxygen lack, a continuous supply of blood being essential for the normal functioning of this organ. An interruption of cerebral circulation of six to eight seconds will produce loss of consciousness. The mental effects of cerebral hypoxia have been frequently described (1) and are well known. As Lennox (2) has pointed out, acute anoxia can produce nervous symptoms not observed in states of chronic oxygen lack and, moreover (3), seizures in epileptic patients can be regularly induced by administration of air deficient in oxygen. Conversely, an increased oxygen pressure will sometimes diminish the number of seizures in an epileptic patient. High oxygen pressures, can, however, induce convulsions, a fact known since 1878 (4). The physiological consequences of oxygen lack (as at high altitudes) and the accompanying intellectual impairment, have been described many years ago (5). It is a constant rather than a rich supply of oxygen that is essential for the normal functioning of the brain, a fact that points to the importance of the regulation, within certain narrow limits, of respiratory activities in the central nervous system and of the various metabolic events dependent on respiration.

The evident dependence of intellectual and other cerebral function on oxygen supply has resulted in much observation

3

concerning the amount of oxygen supplied to the brain in health and disease, and investigation of neuronal respiratory mechanisms.

The brain, which normally derives its energy almost entirely from oxidative processes, consumes oxygen at a rate which is among the highest in the body. A mean value, in normal man, is 3.5 ml. per hundred grams per minute (6). Hou (7) calculated, over thirty years ago, that 5.6 - 7.8 ml. oxygen are consumed by 100 g. dog brain per minute, whilst Kety and Schmidt (8), using their nitrous oxide technique, have found that young adult human brain consumes 3.3 ml. oxygen per 100 g. per minute, indicating that the brain consumes one fifth of the total oxygen consumed by the body. Folch (9) has calculated that during the first four years of life more than one-half of the total oxygen consumption of the body is by the brain.

Estimation of the rate of oxygen consumption by the whole brain *in vivo* is readily calculated from measurements of the cerebral blood flow and the concentration difference for oxygen between arterial and cerebral venous blood.

This flow through the brain is so fast, about 750 ml. per minute in man, that studies of arteriovenous differences are only useful for substances that are formed, or taken up, rapidly. For a variety of substances taken up relatively slowly by the brain, though essential for its metabolism, arteriovenous differences are too small for accurate assessment.

In spite of large changes in blood flow, cerebral oxygen consumption remains constant, except in certain very abnormal conditions. Cerebral blood flow is predominantly dependent on cerebrovascular tone and so is greatly affected by carbon dioxide tension. Inhalations of low concentrations of carbon dioxide produce a cerebral vasodilation and consequent increase of cerebral blood flow of about 75% (Table I) (13). In fact, addition of carbon dioxide to inspired air brings about toleration of fairly low oxygen tensions (14). Conversely, a fall in blood carbon dioxide tension, produced, for example, by hyperventilation, results in constriction of cerebral blood vessels, and a reduction in blood flow that may give rise to cerebral hypoxia with accompanying light headedness. and even loss of consciousness. Other factors influencing cerebral blood flow are changes of hydrogen ion concentration (whose effects are difficult to distinguish from those of altered carbon

TABLE 1

Conditions in man	Cerebral blood flow	Cerebral oxygen consumption	Ref.
		ml./100g./min.	
Normal Awake	54	3.3	10
Normal Asleep	65	3.4	10
CO_2 (5-7%)	93	3.3	10
O_2 (85-100%)	45	3.2	10
O_2 (10%)	73	3.2	10
Increased intracranial pressure	34	2.8	10
Primary polycythemia	25	3.0	10
Anemia	79	3.3	10
Cerebral arteriosclerosis	41	2.8	10
Cerebral hemangioma	164	3.3	10
Essential hypertension	54	3.4	10
Diabetic acidosis	45	2.7	10
Diabetic coma	65	1.7	10
Insulin hypoglycemia	61	2.6	10
Insulin coma	63	1.9	10
Pentothal anaesthesia	60	2.1	10
Schizophrenia	54	3.3	10
Uremic subjects	50	2.3	11
Myxedema	40	2.8	12

dioxide tension) and oxygen tension. Lowering the oxygen content of inhaled air results in an increased cerebral blood flow and
it is concluded (10) that anoxia has as powerful a dilator action
on cerebral vessels as a 5% concentration of carbon dioxide.
High tensions of oxygen bring about a decrease in blood flow;
thus inhalation of 100% oxygen produces some constriction of
cerebral vessels and a 13% reduction in cerebral blood flow (13).
It has been stated for this reason that inhalation of 100% oxygen
may actually cause an increase of an area of cerebral infarction.
Others feel that the increased arterial oxygen tension leads to a
reduced area of infarction.* According to Schmidt, Kety and
Pennes (17), cerebral blood flow tends to vary with cerebral
metabolic rate so that the arteriovenous oxygen tension difference
remains approximately constant. Thus, in metrazole induced
convulsions, for example, there is an increased blood flow that
parallels a rise in cerebral metabolism.

Examples of the fact that cerebral oxygen consumption may
remain constant under conditions where there are extensive
changes of blood flow are shown in Table I. Indeed there is
little change in the oxygen consumption of the brain with change

*[The subject of control of cerebral blood flow is fully discussed by Schmidt (15)
and Lassen (16).]

of rate of blood flow unless this is reduced below 50% of its normal value (18).

Cerebral oxygen consumption is, however, definitely affected in a number of pathological conditions where there is but little change in rate of blood flow (Table I). In coma of varied aetiology there is a large decrease in rate of cerebral oxygen consumption; mean values of 2.2 ml. oxygen uptake per 100 g. per minute have been reported for uremic subjects (11) and 1.7 for patients in diabetic coma (19) where a good correlation was found between depth of coma and cerebral oxygen consumption. Similarly, in experiments on the metabolism of the brain in monkey (17) it has been shown that, under light barbiturate anaesthesia, a mean value of 3.7 ml. oxygen consumed per 100 g. per minute (obtained with the animal in good condition, exhibiting spontaneous movements) falls to 1.7 ml. in animals whose reflexes were absent and which had to be artificially ventilated. It is reported (20) that in patients with various degrees of dementia (neurosyphilitic) a correlation exists between functional derangement of the brain and a reduction in cerebral oxygen uptake.

Reductions in cerebral oxygen consumption occur (16) in patients with organic dementia, brain damage and oedema, hepatic coma, hypoglycaemia, or acute hypertensive encephalopathy. The degree of impairment of "consciousness" parallels the reduction in oxygen consumption.

Cerebral oxygen consumption is depressed by over 30% in pentothal anaesthesia (21,22) and in acute alcoholic intoxication (23).

No detectable changes in cerebral oxygen consumption occur, however, in sleep (Table 1) (24), or during mental arithmetic exercises (25), or in patients with schizophrenia (26). It should not be concluded that where there is no fall in over-all oxygen consumption of the brain there are no physiological changes in that organ. It is known, for example, that changes in electrical activity of the brain may occur with concentrations of anaesthetics that have no apparent effect on cerebral circulation. Where respiration is depressed the E.E.G. (activity as seen in the electroencephalogram) is slowed and may be absent from parts of the brain (27,28). The E.E.G. of sleep differs from that seen in coma. Most kinds of experimentally induced convulsions are associated with increased cerebral metabolic rates (17,29). Epileptics, however, during periods free from seizures show no difference in cerebral oxygen uptake from the normal (30). Oxygen is needed for the maintenance of convulsive activity, as its absence causes arrest of electrical activity of brain cortex (31), complete cessation of electrical activity occurring in dogs breathing 4% oxygen (32). Increased cerebral circulatory rate in convulsions begins shortly after the onset of local neuronal discharge and applies to those parts involved in the seizure (33). It is evident that increased cerebral oxygen consumption may follow the convulsion and is not necessarily responsible for it. Convulsions can occur, however, during hypoglycaemia, hypoxia and cyanide poisoning. Interference, therefore, with the energy metabolism in some parts of the brain may be directly involved in the development of seizures. During ischaemia and hypoxia of the brain, which can cause functional paralysis followed by irreversible damage due to lack of oxidative energy, the first mental disturbances and alterations of the E.E.G. coincide with diminution of total cerebral oxygen consumption (34).

Experiments in which the circulation of dogs was completely stopped and subsequently, after varying intervals, re-initiated were carried out by Heymans and Bouckaert (35). After 30 minutes of anoxia, neurons in the brain were still able to regain their function (respiration, vasomotor and pupillary reflexes). Oxygen lack longer than five minutes resulted in the cessation of cerebral function but within this interval full recovery (except for blindness) could take place. Obviously various parts of the nervous system differ in their sensitivities to oxygen lack and abilities to recover.

McFarland and his colleagues (36,37) have shown that, under anoxia, there is a decrease in efficiency of ocular movements, attributed to diminished oxygen supply to subcortical as well as cortical tissue. They consider that changes in eye movements can be used to detect early effects of oxygen deprivation. Oxygen deficiency produces a marked decrease in visual discrimination which can be alleviated by the addition of 3% carbon dioxide which doubtless acts by improving cerebral blood flow (Gellhorn, 38). According to McFarland (39) the cerebral vasodilation and increased blood flow known to occur in anoxia cannot fully compensate for the diminished oxygen tension. The final result "is an impairment of sensory and mental function and integration, the cortical cells apparently suffering more than other parts of the central nervous system."

Evidence indicates that deprivation of oxygen acts selectively on different parts of the nervous system (40). Cyanide or carbon monoxide poisoning has selective effects, resulting in more consistent degeneration of neurons in the globus pallidus and parts of the cerebellum and cerebral white matter than elsewhere in the brain (41).

Most hormones have little or no effect on the oxygen consumption of the brain (6). Adrenaline, however, when given intravenously in doses sufficient to produce a significant rise in blood pressure, gives rise to increased cerebral oxygen consumption (42). In severe hyperthyroidism, however, the rate of oxygen consumption by the brain is reported as normal even in cases where total body oxygen consumption is increased by 50% above the normal (43,44). In myxedema (Table 1) cerebral respiration rate is reported to be lower than the normal.

In hypothermia the cerebral oxygen consumption rate decreases with fall of temperature at an almost linear rate. The toleration of ischemia increases linearly as the temperature of the brain is reduced (34).

The normal blood flow and oxygen saturation of the blood seem to be more than adequate to supply the brain's respiratory demands   According to Lennox (45) the oxygen content of the blood leaving the brain is about 60% of the saturation value

The evidence obtained from studies of cerebral oxygen consumption *in vivo*, both in health and in disease, leads to the conclusion that a fall in the rate of oxygen consumption is associated with functional cerebral disturbances, but that a constancy of the rate does not necessary imply that there is no change in the functional behaviour of the brain   Moreover, it is evident that local changes may occur in various parts of the central nervous system that may have far reaching effects on the behaviour of the brain, but which are not reflected by any marked change in its over-all oxygen consumption   It is a striking fact that the brain is so regulated that constancy of the rate of oxygen consumption is obtained in a variety of conditions affecting blood flow and oxygen tension. This constancy of rate of oxygen uptake points to the importance, for the normal metabolism of the brain cell, of a constant supply of respiratory energy.

OXYGEN CONSUMPTION OF THE BRAIN *IN VITRO*

Some of the earliest results on the respiratory activity of the brain *in vitro* are due to Warburg and his colleagues (46), who had in 1923 introduced the tissue slice technique for the study of *in vitro* metabolism. Rat brain cortex in presence of a glucose-Ringer medium at 37°C yielded an oxygen quotient (Q_{O_2} = cmm. O_2 taken up per mg. dry weight tissue per hour) of 10.7 while retina gave the high figure of 30.7. Although higher figures for the Q_{O_2} of brain cortex slices have been recorded, both in normal physiological media (47) and in media fortified by the addition of a variety of substances that are consumed by the brain (48), the values are usually lower than those calculated from those obtained by the study of the brain *in vivo*. Estimates of *in vitro* respiratory rates of whole brain, made by Elliott (49), approximate to the values found *in vivo* in conditions of diminished functional activity but are considerably less than normal values *in vivo* (about one half). Some typical values are quoted in Table 2. It is evident that respiratory rates of brain tissue *in vitro*, examined in normal

TABLE 2

Oxygen Uptake by Whole Brain In Vivo and In Vitro (49)

	Q_{O_2}			
	In vitro	*In vivo*		
	Estimated	Lack of reflexes	Normal	Reference
Cat	6.8	6.9	12-15	29
		Depressed		
Monkey	5.9	(Hemorrhage)	11.1	17
		5.6		
		Coma		
Man	4.8	Diabetic Insulin	9.9	19,8
		5.1 5.7		

physiological media, do not reflect the rates obtained in the brain *in situ*. Nevertheless, it is possible by stimulation of isolated brain tissue, by alteration of the cationic concentrations in the medium surrounding the brain tissue, or by electrical stimulation, to increase respiratory rates to approximately those found *in vivo*.

Dixon and Meyer (50) working with ox brain have found that the respiration of minced brain cortex in presence of glucose is about half that of the sliced tissue. The respiration of other parts of the brain (cornu ammonis, globus pallidus, thalamus, cerebellar cortex) in presence of glucose is very greatly decreased, on mincing, from the values obtained with slices. Various parts of the central nervous system have different susceptibilities to mechanical injury so far as total respiration is concerned. This seems particularly the case with the larger cells of the trigeminal ganglion. Examination (50) of the respiratory rates of slices of various parts of ox brain in presence of glucose gave results quoted in Table 3 and shows that, under similar experimental conditions, respiratory rates *in vitro* are by no means uniform for all parts of the brain.

TABLE 3

OXYGEN UPTAKE IN CMM. PER GRAM
WET WEIGHT TISSUE (OX BRAIN) PER HOUR (50)

Cerebral cortex	1700
Cerebellar cortex	2550
Corpus striatum	1980
Cornu ammonis	1260
Thalamus	1170
Globus pallidus	360

The respiratory activity of white matter is less than that of grey matter, usually about one-half to one-third, but smaller estimates have been given. Brookens *et al.* (51), using a capillary micro-respirometer, state that respiration values for various portions of white matter range from 650 to 1800 cmm. O_2 per gram per hour and for grey matter from 800 to 2500 cmm. O_2 per gram per hour. Krebs and Rosenhagen (52) give a range of 2.8 - 4.6 as the Q_{O_2} for rabbit brain white matter while the Q_{O_2} of grey matter of basal ganglia is given as 7.6 - 9.9. Elliott and Heller (53) quote the results given in Table 4. They conclude from results of respiration measurements and estimations of cell density in cerebral cortex, cerebellar cortex, white matter and glial tumours, that the respiration of cerebral cortex is largely due to the neurons present. Moreover, they calculate (53) that the average neuron in the cerebral cortex exhibits more metabolic activity than that in the cerebellar cortex, whilst the non-neuronal cell of white matter respires more actively than the average neuron of cerebellar cortex. Oligodendrocytes account for most of the respiration of white matter (109).

TABLE 4

RESPIRATORY ACTIVITIES OF BRAIN TISSUES
(IN PHOSPHATE-RINGER MEDIA)

		Q_{O_2}
Cat	Cerebral cortex	12.4
	Cerebellar cortex	10.6
	Corpus callosum	2.5
Dog	Cerebral cortex	13.1
	Cerebellar cortex	10.8
	Corpus callosum	2.2
Man	Cerebral cortex	10.6
	Temporal white matter	2.7
	Cerebellar white matter	1.2

It is thus evident that respiratory activities of brain cells may differ according to their location in the brain. The values quoted refer to tissues studied *in vitro*; their magnitudes in the functioning brain may be very different and new techniques must be devised to measure them.

RESPIRATION OF BRAIN STIMULATED *IN VITRO*

The respiration of isolated brain tissue, incubated in a normal physiological (glucose containing) medium, may be increased by two methods to values approximating to those found *in vivo*: (a) alteration of the cationic composition, notably the K^+/Ca^{++} ratio, of the medium in which the brain slice is incubated; (b) application of electrical impulses.

It was shown many years ago by Dickens and Greville (54) and by Ashford and Dixon (55) that increasing the potassium ion concentration of the medium, in which a brain slice is immersed, to 100 meq/l (which is approximately the concentration of potassium ions in the nerve cell) brings about a marked increase in the rate of respiration, approaching double that of the normal in a glucose medium. That the stimulating effect is due to increase in the K^+/Ca^{++} ratio rather than to the absolute magnitude of the potassium ion concentration, is demonstrated by the fact that an equal stimulation may occur by removal of calcium ions from a medium containing the usual (5 meq/l) concentration of potassium ions (56). This phenomenon does not occur in a brain homogenate or mince; it is evident that it is linked with the integrity of the brain cell membranes.

It was equally well known that the respiration of isolated muscle and peripheral nerve is increased on electrical stimulation. Winterstein (57) showed that application of electrical impulses to isolated frog spinal cord led to an increase in its respiration. Bronk and Brink (58), in fact, demonstrated that the increment in the rate of oxygen uptake of frog nerve carrying impulses at the rate of 50 impulses/second is highly narcotic sensitive. McIlwain (59,41) showed that application of electrical impulses to the isolated brain tissue (in the form of slices), in a physiological medium, brings about an increased rate of respiration, approximately double the normal value.

There is little doubt that both methods of respiratory stimulation have a common basis, namely cationic displacements at the brain cell membrane. What is important, however, is the fact that the stimulated respiration of isolated brain tissue has the magnitude of brain respiration *in vivo* and possesses some of the characteristic features of brain *in vivo* such as response to drug action. If the working hypothesis be correct that the stimulated brain slice is an approximation, so far as its biochemical characteristics are concerned, to the functioning brain, that is, to brain tissue *in vivo*, stimulated by sensory impulses, then such material makes it possible to study, more accurately than has hitherto been possible, the effects of chemical and physical changes in the environment on the behaviour of the central nervous system. It must be borne in mind, however, that brain slices, under the best experimental conditions obtained so far, do not show all the electrophysiological responses to stimulation nor the spontaneous activity associated with brain *in vivo*. Nevertheless, even as an approximation to the *in vivo* condition, they are able to yield valuable biochemical data that bear upon the properties of the functioning brain.

Geiger (60) has used a perfusion technique on whole brain, separated chemically from the rest of the body while maintaining its nervous connections with it. The advantages of such a system are somewhat diminished by the use of a "simplified blood" which results in a change of the rates of oxygen consumption, glucose utilization etc. from those prevailing in the intact animal with normal blood composition. The technique represents, however, a still closer approximation to conditions in the living animal and much valuable data has already been obtained with it. Electrical excitability is retained and the effects of addition or omission of substrates to the perfusing "blood" may be examined.

SUBSTRATES OF BRAIN RESPIRATION

It was known many years ago that glucose, fructose and mannose increase the oxygen uptake of excised minced brain tissues (61, 62, 63). Quastel and Wheatley (63) studied the oxidation of brain tissues that had been allowed to deplete itself largely of oxidisable material, prior to the addition of a substrate, by autoxidation for two or three hours. They showed that of all sugars tested, glucose, fructose and mannose had the largest effects in restoring the rate of respiration to nearly the initial value. Galactose had a small effect but mannitol and the pentoses were inert. They also showed that the addition of lactate and pyruvate to minced brain tissue, partly depleted of metabolites by autoxidation, restored the rate of respiration to almost the initial level. Peters and his colleagues (64) used finely minced brain tissue from pigeons suffering from artificially induced avitaminosis B_1, and they demonstrated that such tissue respires at a smaller rate than normally in presence of glucose or lactate and that the addition of vitamin B_1 *in vitro* restores the ability of the brain to respire at a normal rate. The effect of the vitamin was found to be intimately associated with the oxidation of pyruvate. Thus it became apparent that the well known neurological disorder resulting from vitamin B_1 deprivation was probably due primarily to a fault in carbohydrate metabolism, the defect being associated with pyruvic acid oxidation.

Besides glucose, and substances linked to glucose breakdown such as α glycerophosphate, and the components of the citric acid cycle which are consumed by the brain, other substances oxidized are L-glutamic acid (63), which was once thought to be the only amino acid burned by the brain, and to a minor extent other amino acids e.g. glycine (65). Butyrate and crotonate are not oxidized at appreciable speeds and the brain has little capacity to abstract and utilize ketone bodies from the blood. Octanoate (66) and palmitate (67), however, undergo oxidation. A variety of amines are oxidized by the brain. This will be the subject of a later chapter.

The brain *in situ* under normal conditions respires almost exclusively at the expense of glucose (68,69,40). The oxygen consumption of the brain corresponds quantitatively to the amount necessary for the oxidation of the whole amount of glucose taken from the blood. With brain slices, incubated aerobically in a glucose-Ringer medium, the amount of glucose disappearing is approximately equal to that expected from the oxygen consumption, assuming complete oxidation, and from the amount of lactic acid formed by aerobic glycolysis (70).

Typical values for the respiration of rat brain cortex slices in the absence and presence of glucose and in a phosphate saline medium at 37° are as follows (71):

$$Q_{O_2}$$
(Mean values over a 2 hour period)

No glucose added	2.89 ± 0.18
With glucose 0.01 M	12.20 ± 0.33

The rate of respiration under these conditions is constant for at least two hours.

Oxidation of glucose by brain *in vivo* is apparently essential for its functional activities. Although lactate and pyruvate are oxidized by brain tissue *in vitro* they cannot preserve or restore function in a manner similar to glucose. Cortical electrical patterns formed during the hypoglycemia produced by hepatectomy, with abdominal evisceration, cannot be restored to normal by administration of lactate, pyruvate, succinate, fumarate or L-glutamate (72). It is possible that the failure of these substances to restore brain function is due to an insufficient rate of transfer from blood to brain.

McIlwain has shown that the increase of respiratory rate by isolated brain cortex on application of electrical impulses takes place with glucose, lactate or pyruvate as substrates but not in presence of succinate (73), or of α ketoglutarate or fumarate (74) or without added substrate. Fructose will replace glucose as a substrate but it will only give comparable effects on electrically stimulated brain respiration at concentrations approximately ten times that of glucose (73).

The results given in Table 5 show the effects of applied electrical impulses on human brain respiration (41).

TABLE 5

Brain slices in glucose-phosphate-saline;	Q_{O_2} Grey matter	White matter
No applied pulses	6.1	2.8
With applied pulses	12.3	4.5

Cationic stimulation of brain cortex respiration takes place with the identical substrates that permit responses to applied electric impulses. Typical results are shown in Table 6 (75).

TABLE 6

Substrate 0.01 M	Q_{O_2} (Rat brain cortex slices) in Ringer-phosphate medium 5mM KCl present	105 mM KCl present
Glucose	12.5	20.5
Fructose	12.6	20.0
Sodium pyruvate	13.2	18.8
Sodium lactate	11.8	16.8
Sodium L-glutamate	7.5	7.0
Sodium succinate	10.8	9.0

There is a close similarity between the effects on brain slice metabolism by applied oscillating electrical impulses or by changed K^+/Ca^{++} ratio in the medium bathing the slice.* In view of the fact that the changes are such as to cause the biochemical behaviour of the isolated tissue to approximate more closely to that of brain in the living animal, it is important to enquire into the mechanisms underlying the phenomenon of stimulation of brain metabolism *in vitro*.

One point of view (41) is that the applied pulses are such as to cause depolarization of the nerve cells, resulting in the migration of sodium and potassium ions normally associated with the transmission of impulses. Restoration of the ions to their normal state would involve the energy derived from respiration.

Exposure of the cells to an environment with a cationic balance different from the normal would also presumably affect ionic movements at the nerve cell membrane resulting in depolarization, with metabolic consequences similar to those due to the application of electric pulses.

---

*McIlwain (115) reports that the 0.1 mM atropine reverses the stimulating action due to applied electric impulses with no effect on the stimulation of respiration due to increased K^+.

This view would be more acceptable if the mechanism were made clear by which changed ionic movements at the brain cell membrane would necessarily involve a change in respiratory rate.

In this connection, mention should be made of recent investigations on the relationship of electrolytes, particularly sodium and potassium ions, to bioelectrical phenomena of peripheral nerve (76,77,78). The results show that maintenance of the polarized state, involving retention of potassium and exclusion of sodium, are dependent on aerobic metabolism (78,134). Thus anoxia (79,76), a respiratory poison such as cyanide (80) or an inhibitor of oxidative phosphorylation such as dinitrophenol (which may leave the rate of oxygen consumption undiminished) causes electrolyte redistribution or changed rates of transfer of sodium and potassium through the nerve cell membrane (81). Keynes concludes that metabolic energy "is necessary to drive the recovery mechanisms responsible for maintaining the high internal potassium and low internal sodium concentrations characteristic of excitable tissue" (81). Metabolic reactions, therefore, exist in nerve that contribute energy for the performance of two processes, one of which excludes sodium whilst the other retains or restores potassium.

In seeking the nature of relationship of ionic movements to energy release Shanes (78) suggests the following mechanisms: (1) Energy is required to maintain nerve cell constituents in a form favouring potassium incorporation or binding over that of sodium. It is known that binding can occur that permits ionic exchange. (2) Energy release preserves selective permeability at the cell surface. (3) Metabolism generates a potential difference which is responsible for ionic differences. (4) Metabolic reactions may operate directly at the cell surface to extrude sodium and take up potassium without necessarily contributing directly to the potential difference. The last mechanism, i.e., the sodium-potassium pump, has the most compelling evidence in its favour (see 443 or 444).

There is no doubt that transport of an ion against a diffusion gradient is an energy dependent process. Metabolic energy, probably in the form of adenosine triphosphate (ATP), is required for active transport to take place. It is conceivable that the reverse process, i.e., the stimulation of respiratory activity by ionic movements at the nerve cell membrane, may occur by the initiation of a series of reactions, possibly involving the accumulation of adenosine diphosphate (ADP) or phosphate ions which are now well known to play key roles in the regulation of respiratory and glycolytic processes. Thus Dawson and Richter (82) have shown that electric stimulation of the brain causes a drop in the content of ATP and a rise of inorganic phosphate in it, whilst Shapot (83) has given evidence that excitation of the brain increases the ADP/ATP ratio. Such reactions by accelerating rate regulating steps in a sequence of respiratory events would result in the stimulation of oxygen uptake of isolated intact brain tissue. The validity of such a conclusion appears likely from a study of the characteristic features of stimulated brain respiration *in vitro*.

Whereas the respiration of unstimulated brain cortex slices in the presence of glucose is but little affected by the presence of malonate, whose well known inhibitory effect on succinate oxidation (84) makes it a potent inhibitor of the citric acid respiratory cycle, potassium-stimulated brain respiration is highly malonate sensitive (85). Results of Takagaki *et al.* (86) on the effects of malonate and of high concentrations of potassium ions on glucose utilization and lactic acid formation by brain cortex slices in presence of glucose are shown in Table 7. They show that malonate suppresses stimulation of respiration but has no adverse effect on

TABLE 7

METABOLISM OF GLUCOSE (3.3 mM) IN GUINEA PIG BRAIN CORTEX SLICES (86)
Values are given in micromoles per gram tissue per hour

Additions	Oxygen uptake	Lactate formed	Glucose utilized	Glucose oxidized (calculated)
Nil	56.5±5.5	17.1±2.6	18.1±2.1	9.6
Malonate 10 mM	42.9±2.1	24.7±4.0	20.5±2.7	8.2
KCl 100 mM	94.4±8.1	59.4±5.9	51.0±4.2	21.3
Malonate 10 mM +KCl 100 mM	36.9±1.8	68.4±1.6	51.2±3.3	17.0

potassium-stimulated aerobic glycolysis. The stimulation of oxygen uptake by brain cortex slices by increased K^+ is shown also by the increased rate of formation of $C^{14}O_2$ when uniformly labelled glucose (i.e., glucose-U-C^{14}) is present as a substrate. It is possible to demonstrate a value of approximately 6.0 for the ratio of potassium-stimulated oxygen uptake to potassium-stimulated glucose breakdown. This is the theoretical value for complete oxidation of glucose to CO_2 and water. A typical experimental result is shown in Table 8 (87).

TABLE 8

EFFECTS OF K^+ ON OXYGEN UPTAKE AND GLUCOSE-U-C^{14} BREAKDOWN TO $C^{14}O_2$ (BY 10 MG. DRY WEIGHT RAT BRAIN CORTEX SLICE IN ONE HOUR)

Micromoles O_2 taken up for glucose consumption*		Micromoles glucose converted to $C^{14}O_2$		Calculated micromoles O_2 taken up, equivalent to glucose converted to $C^{14}O_2$	
5 mM KCl	105 mM KCl	5 mM KCl	105 mM KCl	5 mM KCl	105 mM KCl
3.4	6.6	0.47	1.05	2.8	6.3

*Corrected for endogenous oxygen uptake.

The malonate inhibition of potassium-stimulated brain cortex respiration which may be reversed by oxaloacetate (87) indicates the important role of the citric acid cycle in stimulated brain respiration. This is shown perhaps more clearly in the results given in Table 9 (88), which indicate that the percentage malonate inhibition of $C^{14}O_2$ from pyruvate-2-C^{14} (i.e., oxidation of the acetyl moiety of the molecule) is considerably greater than that from pyruvate-1-C^{14} (i.e., where only the carboxyl group is labelled) both in the absence and presence of an increased potassium ion concentration. That malonate inhibits the latter process indicates that part of the $C^{14}O_2$ derived from pyruvate-1-C^{14} is

TABLE 9

EFFECTS OF KCl AND MALONATE ON PYRUVATE METABOLISM IN RAT BRAIN CORTEX SLICES

Substrate	Qo_2		$C^{14}O_2$ formed in 1 hr. (Expressed as counts/min./mg dry weight)	
	5 mM KCl	105 mM KCl	5 mM KCl	105 mM KCl
(1) Pyruvate-1-C^{14}				
(a) without 10 mM malonate	14.2	19.8	1166	2008
(b) with 10 mM malonate	8.0	9.2	903	1342
(2) Pyruvate-2-C^{14}				
(a) without 10 mM malonate	14.2	19.8	481	1040
(b) with 10 mM malonate	8.0	9.2	258	336

formed after its fixation and metabolism by the citric acid cycle.

Just as potassium-stimulated brain respiration is highly malonate sensitive so is electrically stimulated respiration.

Neither potassium stimulation nor malonate inhibition occurs in brain homogenates respiring in glucose media. Evidently the stimulation of metabolism by changed cationic (K^+/Ca^{++}) balance is inherently associated with events taking place at the brain cell membrane. It has to be emphasized that the stimulating effect on neuronal respiration may also be brought about by complete deprivation of calcium ions from the medium bathing the brain cortex slices without increase of the normal Ringer concentration of potassium. Hence a change of K^+/Ca^{++} balance must be regarded as a significant factor affecting neuronal respiration.

Potassium stimulation of neuron metabolism secures other phenomena of which one or two may be appropriately considered here. The presence of potassium ions (27 meq./l) brings about a large increase in the rate of synthesis of acetylcholine by brain cortex slices respiring in a glucose-containing medium, the potassium effect being neutralized by the addition of calcium ions (89). This effect is absent (or diminished) in brain homogenates. Rowsell (90) has pointed out that the application of electrical impulses to brain slices has a precisely similar effect, the release of free acetylcholine from its "bound" state and an acceleration in the rate of synthesis of acetycholine. Again, the stimulation of aerobic glycolysis, effected by increased K^+ (see Table 7), is shown also by application of electrical impulses to brain slices *in vitro* (91). This phenomenon has its parallel in the increased formation of lactic acid in the brain in the living animal when brain excitation occurs (82,92,93).

These facts serve to demonstrate the many features in common between the effects of changed K^+/Ca^{++} balance on brain metabolism *in vitro* and those of applied electric impulses and the approximation of some of the metabolic events in stimulated brain slices to those of brain in the living animal.

Results such as those shown in Table 9 and those from quantitative studies of the conversion in brain cortex of radioactive glucose and fructose into radioactive amino acids (88), of which more will be mentioned later, lead to the conclusion that one rate limiting step, which is accelerated by increased K^+/Ca^{++} is the conversion in brain of pyruvic acid into acetyl-CoA, the oxidation of which is accomplished by the citric acid cycle. Whether the effect of the ionic change on this oxidative process is direct or indirect is not known for certain at present, but it is likely to be indirect as it does not occur in a brain homogenate. Presumably it may be accomplished, as already mentioned, by an effect of ionic balance at the nerve cell membranes on the formation of ADP or phosphate ions. This is a matter for further investigation. Doubtless other changes that may, under various circumstances, become rate limiting are also affected. Thus there is evidence that the oxidations of other ketonic acids, e.g., α-ketoglutaric acid and oxaloacetic acid, are also accelerated by increased K^+. Whether these are all reflections of one underlying phenomenon is as yet uncertain.

It is likely that brain lipids play an important role in electrolyte balance in the brain cell. In view of the significance in brain oxidative metabolism of phospholipids, to which reference will be made later, and in view also of the disturbance in lipid chemistry in certain diseases of the nervous system, some reference will be made to recent work on this subject. Koch and Pike (132) seem to have been the first to draw attention to a possible role of brain lipids on electrolyte balance as they found large amounts of sodium and potassium in alcohol-ether extracts of the brain and in lecithin, cephalin and sulphatides of the brain. They claimed that a substantial part of sodium and potassium are combined with lipids in brain. Folch (132) ultimately made clear that mammalian brain contains at least three different acidic lipids and it was possible to calculate that, in adult bovine brain, cerebron sulphuric acid, phosphatidyl serine and diphosphoinositide combine with as much as one quarter of all the cations present. Further work by Folch and his colleagues (133) showed that the cations Na^+, K^+, Ca^{++}, Mg^{++}, may compete with each other for combination with lipids. It is evident that changes in lipid structures may affect electrolyte balance which in turn will effect the energetics and functional activity of the brain cell. Probably such lipid structures constitute much of the brain cell membranes that have a controlling effect on electrolyte distribution and cell energetics.

BRAIN RESPIRATION AND AGE

Very early studies showed the presence of cytochrome oxidase in brain. Those of Vernon (94) showed that indophenol (or cytochrome) oxidase activity of the brain in various animal species varies inversely with the size of the animal, being greater in mice, for example, than in dogs. It was suggested (95) that the inverse relationship may be due to varying proportions of grey to white matter in the brain of these animals, the smaller animals having the greater proportion of grey matter. The respiratory rate of cerebral cortex (per unit weight of tissues) decreases, rather irregularly however, with increasing size of the animal (96). There is no relation of *in vitro* respiration rate of cerebral tissue to the body weight of individual animals in any species. Histochemical studies (109) have shown that cytochrome oxidase activity in human brain cortex is about one tenth that of rat brain cortex (for equal amounts of tissue).

The strong inhibitive action of cyanide on normal respiration of the brain points to cytochrome oxidase being quantitatively the most important mechanism in the brain for oxygen activation. Potter *et al.* (97) have observed that this enzyme is low in activity at birth (in the rat) and increases steadily during the first month of life. It is presumably absent in the early stage of fetal development. These facts are to be correlated with observations on the rat (98) and on the dog (99) which have led to the conclusion that newer parts of the brain respire at a slower rate than the older portions at the time of birth. As growth continues, these relative positions are reversed and the metabolic rates of the newer parts of the brain take the lead. In contrast with the newborn animal, the adult rat exhibits the highest rate of metabolism in the phyletically newest parts of the brain (40). The increasing rate of metabolism of the brain as a whole, with age, is to be attributed largely to the increasing rate in the newer parts of the brain during early life (40). In the pig, born in a more mature stage than the rat, the maximum rise of cytochrome oxidase takes place during the terminal quarter of gestation and at birth its value is the same as that in the adult (100).

The stimulatory effect of potassium ions on aerobic nerve metabolism is small in infant (rat) brain (101), the response to potassium increasing from the time of birth to forty days of age.

The inhibitory effect of malonate on brain respiration also increases with age during the first ten days of post natal life (102). Himwich (40) points out that adult cerebral tissues show a larger response to a rise in temperature than infant cerebral tissue.

It is evident that the characteristic features of adult brain metabolism develop relatively slowly and are not present in the initial stages of brain development. During this period there are no signs of transmission of nerve impulses in the brain. There is a close association between functional development of the brain and a variety of enzymic constituents. Not only is this the case with certain oxidative systems, but with cholinesterase (103) and carbonic anhydrase (104).*

Glycolysis plays an important role as an energy yielding system in the early stages of brain development, but, after birth, respiration, i.e., rate of oxygen consumption, increases until it becomes the major source of energy to the brain. This change does not take place uniformly through the brain but commences at the spinal cord and eventually reaches the cerebral cortex. The relative importance of brain respiration for energy supply to the brain at different ages presumably determines relative vulnerabilities at different ages to anoxia. Thus rats survive 50 minutes in nitrogen on their day of birth but only three or four minutes from eleven days of age onwards (41).

Application of electrical pulses, like exposure to increased K^+/Ca^{++}, has less effect on the respiratory rate of brain cortex of newly born rats than on that of adult animals. Development of the various features that characterize the metabolism of the brain, and therefore its functional activity, is not uniform; electrical activity, for example, may be present when full maturity has not been reached. This becomes an important matter when considering the effects on cerebral development of nutritional or enzymatic defects.

The oxygen consumption of the human brain varies with age, it being highest in young children. Data accumulated by Kety (106) are shown in Table 10. There is a rapid fall in the cerebral

---

*For further information on this interesting topic the reader is referred to Sperry (105), McIlwain (41) and the Symposium, *Biochemistry of the Developing Nervous System.* Ed. H. Waelsch. Academic Press. 1955.

TABLE 10

CHANGES OF CEREBRAL BLOOD FLOW AND CEREBRAL OXYGEN
CONSUMPTION WITH AGE (IN MAN)

Mean age	Cerebral blood flow (ml./100 g./min.)	Cerebral O_2 consumption (ml./100 g./min.)	Reference
5	104	5.1	106
10	90	5.3	107
13	68	4.0	108
19	60	3.7	43
30	53	3.4	110
63	51	3.4	111
68	43	2.4	112
93	39	2.7	113

circulation about the time of puberty which continues through adolescence. There then is a more gradual but continuous decline in the cerebral blood flow through middle and old age. Cerebral oxygen consumption also falls rapidly at first and then more gradually with advancing years. There is as yet no clear explanation for the fall in oxygen consumption of the brain with increasing age (106). Possibly this is due to a progressive decrease in ratio of neurons to glial cells (114) but it may be that the cerebral derangement in aging lies in the diminished metabolic demands of the brain, which could be the result of loss of neurons or deterioration of essential cellular components or perhaps "a lessened functional demand as a result of the psychological and social changes which attend the aging process" (106).

CARBOHYDRATE METABOLISM OF THE BRAIN

Glucose Utilization *In Vivo*

The respiratory quotient of the brain *in vivo* was known many years ago to be about unity, pointing to the probability that carbohydrate is the main fuel of the brain. This conclusion was supported by the fact that oxygen consumption is approximately equivalent to the glucose disappearance in the passage of blood through the brain, assuming complete oxidation of glucose (68). In an analysis of a variety of estimations on the human brain *in vivo* of the oxygen-glucose utilization ratio (which is theoretically equal to 6.0 for complete oxidation of glucose to carbon dioxide and water), Kety (6) finds an average ratio of 5.5 with a standard error of 0.13. The difference from the theoretical value is significant and indicates that part of the glucose is metabolized other than by complete oxidation. The average value for normal glucose utilization by the human brain is about 5 mg. per 100 g. brain per minute (6).

An estimate (69) has been made that about 85% of the glucose obtained by the brain from the blood is oxidized to carbon dioxide, about 13% is converted to lactate and 2% to pyruvate. However, it is now known that some glucose is transformed into amino acids in the brain, though the extent of this process *in vivo* is at present unknown. It would seem correct to conclude that much of the glucose disappearing from the blood into the brain is fully oxidized, but that a small (and possibly variable) fraction, depending upon a variety of circumstances, is converted into other substances.

Hypoglycaemia and Mental Function

In hypoglycaemic coma in man, the brain continues to use oxygen at about half the normal rate when the blood glucose has dropped considerably and the amount utilized is negligible (26). It is, therefore, clear that in the absence of exogenous glucose the brain may continue to respire and to survive for a short time. It remains evident, however, that under normal circumstances glucose is the chief source of fuel for the brain.

A significant decrease in the blood glucose level is consistently associated with a disturbed cerebral and mental behaviour. Many studies on insulin hypoglycaemia and coma have shown good correlation between blood glucose level and the mental state (26, 116,117) as well as E.E.G. patterns (118). Moreover, intravenous injection of glucose promptly restores mental function in insulin coma of short duration.

A great many substances have been tested to see if they will replace glucose in restoring consciousness in hypoglycaemic man. Fructose, galactose, lactose, insulin, hexosediphosphate, lactate, pyruvate, ethanol are all ineffective. In the hepatectomized animal, restoration of normal behaviour or of normal cortical electrical patterns cannot be brought about by lactate, pyruvate succinate, fumarate, glycerol, acetate or glutamate.

Weil-Malherbe (119) has demonstrated arousal from insulin coma in a number of patients by administration of glutamate, arginine, glycine and succinate and considers that their action is associated with a rise in blood adrenaline and blood glucose. Mayer-Gross and Walker (120) found that both glutamate and glycine were effective in restoring consciousness to many patients under deep insulin coma, a rise in blood sugar taking place. Yet certain patients, who experienced a rise in blood sugar, still remained comatose.

Mannose and maltose restore normal behaviour and cerebral activity to hepatectomized animals (121,72) but possibly they do so after preliminary conversion to glucose.

It should be noted that under normal conditions the glucose content of the brain is somewhat (by 25-40%) lower than that of blood. Variations in the blood glucose concentration bring about parallel variations in the brain, but brain glucose concentration does not increase to the same extent as that in blood if the latter concentration is elevated far beyond the normal range of variation (122). For example, when the blood contains 800 mg.% glucose, the brain contains 300 mg.% and the latter is only increased slightly by doubling the glucose concentration. Movement of glucose from blood involves the phenomenon of active transport of glucose into the cell, a phenomenon that has received much attention in the case of isolated intestine (123) but, as yet, relatively little in the case of the central nervous system. Granting that active transport of glucose takes place in brain, it is evident that penetration of glucose will depend on respiratory conditions in the brain cell and possibly upon other factors including electrolyte distribution and concentration.

Diabetic Coma

Cerebral oxygen uptake in diabetic coma is reduced by 20-50%. Yet under these conditions blood glucose may be as high as 300 mg.%. The decreased cerebral respiration is clearly not due to lack of glucose in the blood. Presumably another factor is operating — possibly blood ketones (19), for injection of aceto-acetate may induce coma. The acidosis of diabetic coma seems not to be the causative factor.

Effects of Glucose Deprivation

Although fairly prompt depressions in synaptic transmissions in the rat spinal cord or stimulated sympathetic ganglion occur in the absence of glucose (124,125), active potentials in the frog brain for as long as three hours in a glucose-free Ringer medium have been recorded (126). Geiger (60) reports, from results on perfusion experiments on whole brain, survival of the brain for a limited period of time when glucose is omitted from the perfusion blood. The brain survives for over an hour if the cerebral flow is increased to three times the normal. The glucose reserve is exhausted within 10-15 minutes and endogenous glycogen does not contribute to the maintenance of oxidations. Normal E.E.G. patterns are recorded in a glucose-free perfusion lasting sometimes for 90 minutes, reflexes are easily obtained and metrazol administration leads to convulsions with the usual increase of oxygen consumption. The oxygen consumption is rather less than with glucose present and the respiratory quotient varies between 0.84 and 0.56 (127). There are losses in brain components, e.g., phospholipids and nucleic acids, during this procedure and amino acids from the brain appear in the blood (128). Evidently the brain can survive for a limited period and maintain its excitability by breakdown of its structural components.

The sensitivity of brain to oxygen and glucose lack was shown many years ago by the fact that the deprivation of brain tissue *in vitro* of both oxygen and glucose for short periods (e.g. five minutes) very greatly decreases the rate of anaerobic glycolysis when glucose is subsequently added to the tissue (129) and, in fact, it was concluded that anaerobiosis, in the absence of glucose, brings about irreparable damage to the brain. It was shown, however (130), that if brain tissue, which has been kept anaerobically for a short time in the absence of glucose, is subsequently exposed to oxygen its power of bringing about anaerobic glycolysis may be almost completely restored. The restoration is doubtless due to resynthesis, by oxidative reactions, of ATP (131), which is depleted under anaerobic conditions in the absence of glucose. It is not known, however, how far deprivation of the brain cell of glucose and oxygen can be maintained without irreversible conditions being established. It is known (136) that the brain cell loses potassium ions when deprived of glucose and oxygen, an electrolyte redistribution being brought about that must entail a variety of other metabolic changes. The outward diffusion of potassium may, however, be reversed if the cell is supplied, under aerobic conditions, with glucose and L-glutamate (137).

The presence of glucose, under aerobic conditions, secures the maintenance not only of ATP, required for a variety of biosynthetic changes in the cell, but of intermediates needed to preserve the normal components of the cell. Larrabee *et al.* (135) point out that though the rate of oxygen consumption by the ganglion is only moderately affected by removal of glucose when function has already ceased, the evidence indicates that endogenous substrates are being oxidized with release of ammonia. The addition of glucose and the subsequent recovery process results in the consumption of this ammonia. This would indicate that brain amino acids are burned in absence of glucose, but doubtless other substances also undergo oxidation.

Glucose-amino Acid Interrelations:
Roles of Adenosine Triphosphate, Adenine Nucleotides and Some Vitamin Components

It will be useful, at this juncture, to comment upon the relationship of glucose breakdown products in the brain cell to the amino acid components present, and on the roles of adenosine triphosphate (ATP), the pyridine nucleotides (DPN and TPN) and vitamin components such as thiamine and pyridoxal.

Whilst the details of the various metabolic reactions involved in glucose breakdown in the cell cannot be described or discussed here in full, the main stages may be outlined.

Carbohydrate is oxidized *via* the intermediate formation of pyruvate whose oxidation is accomplished by operation of the citric acid cycle. The free energy changes are shown in Table 11,

TABLE 11

FREE ENERGY CHANGES IN THE OXIDATION OF PYRUVATE BY THE CITRIC ACID CYCLE
(FIGURES IN BRACKETS REFER TO FREE ENERGY CHANGES ΔG IN KILOCALORIES
PER MOLE REACTANTS AT 25°)

	Pyruvate	
(−60)	↓ + CoA	*Oxidation*
	Acetylcoenzyme A + CO_2	
(−7.5)	↓ Oxaloacetate	
	Citrate	
(+2.0)	↓ −H_2O	
	Cis − Aconitate	
(−0.4)	↓ +H_2O	
	Isocitrate	
(−54)	↓	*Oxidation*
	α ketoglutarate + CO_2	
(−70)	↓ H_2O	*Oxidation*
	Succinate + CO_2	
(−35)	↓	*Oxidation*
	Fumarate	
(−0.9)	↓ H_2O	
	Malate	
(−44)	↓	*Oxidation*
	Oxaloacetate	

details of which are supplied in a survey by Krebs and Kornberg (138). The free energy of the oxidation of substrates usually becomes available (except with α ketonic acids) when the reduced forms of the pyridine nucleotides (diphosphopyridine nucleotide, DPN, and triphosphopyridine nucleotide, TPN) are oxidized by the flavoproteins and cytochrome components in accordance with the following reactions (139):

1. Reduced pyridine nucleotide and flavoprotein
   = reduced flavoprotein + pyridine nucleotide
2. Reduced flavoprotein + 2 ferricytochrome
   = flavoprotein + 2 ferrocytochrome
3. 2 Ferrocytochrome + O = 2 ferricytochrome + H_2O

The total effect of these reactions is the oxidation of reduced pyridine nucleotide, thus:

4. Reduced pyridine nucleotide + O = pyridine nucleotide + H_2O
   (standard free energy change, — 52 kg. cal.).

This scheme is simpler than actually occurs, as a variety of flavoproteins and cytochrome components are involved and may include other factors such as vitamins K and E (140). In fact, according to Martius, vitamin K may replace flavoprotein. Various reactions involved in the metabolism of pyruvate are shown in Fig. 1. Reactions of the α ketonic acids are of particular importance, as they give rise by transamination to corresponding amino acids.

The following values (in micromoles per gram tissue) are the cerebral concentrations of intermediates (in the citric acid cycle) in rats which have been fasted for 24 hours, anaesthetized and the brains rapidly removed and frozen (41): Pyruvate 1.96; citrate 0.28; isocitrate 0.03, α ketoglutarate 1.30; succinate 0.34; fumarate 1,20; malate 0.24; oxaloacetate 0.64. Whether these values represent steady states representative of those in the living brain is unknown, for under the experimental conditions that were used, lactic acid had accumulated.

Reactions of α Ketonic Acids

Many amino acids (141) can transfer their α amino groups to α ketoglutarate and to pyruvate by transamination, a process involving a reversible exchange of amino and keto groups, thus:

$$R.CH_2CHNH_2.COOH + COOH.CO.CH_2.CH_2COOH \rightleftharpoons$$
$$R.CH_2.COCOOH + COOH.CHNH_2.CH_2.CH_2.COOH$$

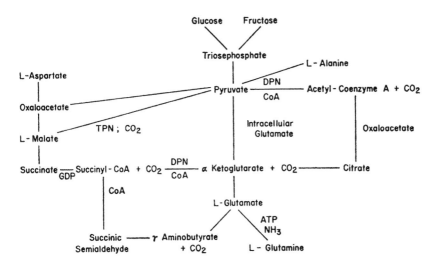

Fig. 1

$$R.CH_2.CHNH_2.COOH + CH_3.CO.COOH \rightleftharpoons$$
$$R.CH_2.CO.COOH + CH_3.CHNH_2.COOH$$

Transamination is a process that requires the participation of the coenzyme, pyridoxal phosphate, whose catalyzed reactions have led Braunstein (142) to consider that it plays a major role in controlling the nitrogen metabolism of the cell. The implications of pyridoxal (vitamin B_6) in metabolism and behaviour of the central nervous system will be considered later.

Oxidation and Oxidative Phosphorylation

The oxidation of α ketoglutarate takes place according to the following reactions:

    1. α Ketoglutarate + CoA + DPN $\rightarrow$
                 Succinyl-CoA + CO_2 + $DPNH_2$,
    2. Succinyl-CoA + guanosine diphosphate + phosphate (P_i)
        $\rightleftharpoons$ Succinate + guanosine triphosphate + CoA
    3. Guanosine triphosphate + adenosine diphosphate (ADP)
        $\rightleftharpoons$ Guanosine diphosphate + adenosine triphosphate (ATP)

Summing up these reactions, the overall change is as follows:

    4. α Ketoglutarate + ADP + P_i + DPN
        $\rightarrow$ Succinate + CO_2 + ATP + $DPNH_2$

These reactions involve the participation of cofactors, thiamine pyrophosphate (TPP) and α lipoic acid, which may react in the following manner (143):

5. $COOH.CH_2.CH_2CO.COOH + TPP = COOH.CH_2.CH_2.CHO.TPP + CO_2$

6. $COOH.CH_2.CH_2.CHO.TPP +$

$$
\begin{array}{c}
S - \overset{\displaystyle R}{\underset{\displaystyle \diagdown}{\overset{\diagup}{CH}}} \\
\Big| \qquad CH_2 \\
S - CH_2 \diagup
\end{array}
$$

α Lipoic acid

$$COOH.CH_2.CH_2.CO-S-\underset{\diagup}{\overset{\displaystyle CHR}{\big|}}\underset{HS-CH_2}{CH_2} + TPP$$

7. $COOH.CH_2.CH_2.CO.S - \underset{HS-CH_2}{\overset{CHR}{\underset{Coenzyme\ A}{\big|}}}$

$CH_2 + CoA.SH \longrightarrow COOH.CH_2.CH_2.CO + HS - \underset{\underset{HS-CH_2}{\big|}}{\overset{CHR}{\underset{\big|}{CH_2}}}$

with $\underset{CoA}{\overset{S}{\big|}}$

8. $HS.CHR$

$$\underset{HS.CH_2}{\overset{CHR}{\underset{\diagup}{\big|}}}CH_2 + DPN \longrightarrow \begin{array}{c} S - \overset{R}{\overset{\diagup}{CH}} \\ \big| \qquad CH_2 \\ S - CH_2 \end{array} + DPNH_2$$

Thus, in these reactions representing the oxidation of α ketoglutaric acid, the following cofactors are intrinsically involved: (a) thiamine, (b) pantothenic acid in the form of coenzyme A, (c) α lipoic acid, (d) nicotinamide in the form of DPN, (e) flavin, in the form of flavoprotein. There is still discussion as to the importance of α lipoic acid in mammalian oxidations.

The same cofactors are involved in the oxidation of pyruvate whose reactions may be represented shortly in the equation:

Pyruvate $+ CoA + DPN =$ Acetyl-CoA $+ DPNH_2 + CO_2$

Accompanying these oxidative mechanisms is the formation of ATP. The free energy change for the oxidation of $DPNH_2$ is about -52 kg. cal, sufficient for the synthesis of at least 3 pyrophosphate bonds (as in ATP), each requiring about 12-14 kg. cal. under physiological conditions. Experiment (144) shows that three pyrophosphate bonds can be formed when one molecule of $DPNH_2$ is oxidized. It is also likely that ATP is synthesized during the oxidations of ferrocytochrome and of reduced flavo-protein.

The mechanisms, therefore, which control the rate of oxygen consumption (i.e., the rates at which $DPNH_2$, reduced flavo-protein and reduced cytochrome react with oxygen) are coupled with the synthesis of ATP from ADP and phosphate ions.

Owing to this circumstance, the reaction

$$DPNH_2 + O \rightarrow DPN + H_2O$$

proceeds at an optimal rate if ADP and phosphate ions are present. It is now well established that phosphate ions and phosphate acceptors (e.g. ADP) have rate limiting functions (145,146,147).

The steady state level of the α ketonic acids in the cell obviously depends on a variety of reactions, whose quantitative aspects under different conditions (e.g., electrolyte balance, oxygen tension, pH, temperature, substrate concentrations, etc.) are not yet well under-stood. For example, oxaloacetate which plays an important role in cell respiration can undergo at least the following reactions:

1. L-malate $+ O \leftrightarrows$ oxaloacetate (DPN linked malic dehydrogenase)
2. Phosphopyruvate $+ CO_2 + ADP \leftrightarrows$ oxaloacetate $+ ATP$
3. Aspartate $+ \alpha$ ketoglutarate $\leftrightarrows$ oxaloacetate $+$ glutamate (transaminase)
4. Oxaloacetate $=$ pyruvate $+ CO_2$
5. Oxaloacetate $+$ acetyl-CoA $\leftrightarrows$ citrate $+$ CoA (condensing enzyme)

Again pyruvate will undergo, in addition to the reactions already mentioned, conversion to malate in the following manner:

$$Pyruvate + CO_2 + TPNH_2 \rightarrow L\text{-malate} + TPN$$

a reaction that proceeds more rapidly in presence of oxygen than in its absence (138,148).

Thus the conversion of glucose into amino acids in the nerve cell, depending on the level of α ketonic acids formed by glucose breakdown, must depend also on a variety of factors, interference or modification of which will have far reaching consequences.

Alternative Pathway of Glucose Oxidation

The most common alternative pathway for glucose oxidation, other than that already mentioned, is the one termed the pentose phosphate cycle or "shunt." This consists of a variety of reactions of which the following may be mentioned here:

1. Glucose-6-phosphate + TPN $\rightleftharpoons$ 6-phosphogluconate + TPNH$_2$
   TPN
2. 6-Phosphogluconate $\rightleftharpoons$ Ribulose-5-phosphate + CO$_2$
3. Ribulose-5-phosphate $\rightleftharpoons$ ribose-5-phosphate
4. Ribulose-5-phosphate $\rightleftharpoons$ xylulose-5-phosphate
5. Ribulose-5-phosphate + xylulose-5-phosphate
   $\rightarrow$ sedoheptulose-7-phosphate + triosephosphate
   Transketolase
6. Sedoheptupose-7-phosphate + triosephosphate
   $\rightarrow$ Erythrose-4-phosphate + fructose-6-phosphate
   Transaldolase
7. Erythrose-4-phosphate + xylulose-5-phosphate
   $\rightarrow$ fructose-6-phosphate + triosephosphate
   Transketolase
8. Fructose-6-phosphate $\rightleftharpoons$ glucose-6-phosphate
   Isomerase

The overall reaction is represented as:

9. Glucose-6-phosphate + 6 TPN $\rightarrow$ triosephosphate + 3 CO$_2$
   + 6 TPNH$_2$

The triosephosphate formed is metabolized via pyruvate or may re-enter the pentose phosphate cycle.

Whilst the pentose phosphate cycle is widespread in many varieties of living cells, its quantitative significance in brain is not yet known with certainty. Its importance lies possibly in the supply of pentose phosphate required in the synthesis of nucleotides and nucleic acid.

The primary hydrogen acceptor in this cycle is TPN (149). The amount of this coenzyme in the brain is small, as shown in the following values for rat brain (150):

DPN 33γ/g; DPNH$_2$ 88γ/g; TPN 2γ/g; TPNH$_2$ 8γ/g.

The low value for total TPN in brain suggests that the pentose phosphate cycle is not very active in brain. Moreover, although the dehydrogenases of the hexose monophosphate pathway are present in brain their activities are about one quarter of those found in an equivalent weight of liver (151). It is reported (515) that TPNH oxidase activity in brain is less than 5% of the DPNH oxidase activity.

It should be noted that the activity of transketolase, which plays an important part in the pentose phosphate cycle, is catalyzed by thiamine pyrophosphate (152). The deprivation of the brain of thiamine, therefore, may affect the "pentose phosphate cycle" as well as the metabolism of pyruvic acid itself.

Glycolysis

The ability of the brain to consume carbohydrate is also seen in its high rate of anaerobic glycolysis (46). In fact, the view was held at one time that oxidation in brain proceeded through the intermediate formation of lactic acid formed during glycolysis. This conclusion was shown to be untenable by the finding that a competitive analogue of lactic acid, viz. tartronic acid, inhibits brain respiration in presence of lactate to a greater extent than in presence of glucose (153). Nicotine, by a mode of behaviour as yet unexplained, has a similar effect (154).

The main stages of glycolysis are well known and are embraced by the Embden-Meyerhof scheme.

They may be given as follows:

1. Glucose + ATP → glucose-6-phosphate + ADP
2. Glucose-6-phosphate → fructose-6-phosphate
3. Fructose-6-phosphate + ATP → fructose 1:6 diphosphate
4. Fructose 1:6 diphosphate → 2 triosephosphate
$$\text{H}_2\text{O}$$
5. Triosephosphate + DPN + ADP + P_i → 3-Phosphoglycerate + DPNH$_2$ + ATP
6. 3-Phosphoglycerate→2:3-diphosphoglycerate→2-phosphoglycerate
7. 2-Phosphoglycerate → phosphopyruvate
8. Phosphopyruvate + ADP → pyruvate + ATP
9. Pyruvate + DPNH$_2$ → lactate + DPN

It is seen that 2 ATP molecules are synthesized during the anaerobic breakdown of glucose i.e. one ATP molecule is formed for each molecule of lactic acid. The yield of ATP by glycolysis is very much less than that obtained from the complete oxidation of a molecule of glucose which yields 38 ATP (155).

The precursors of pyruvic acid are phosphopyruvic acid and phosphoglyceric acid, whose formation is dependent on the availabilities and concentrations of ADP and inorganic phosphate (Pi). The concentration of ADP or Pi may therefore have a determining effect on pyruvic acid formation and on the course and speed of respiration.

In the overall estimate of the course of metabolic events in the cell, such ratios as ATP/ADP, DPN/DPNH$_2$, TPN/TPNH$_2$, etc., are as important for the direction of and speed of chemical events in the nervous system as the actual presence of the cytochrome components, cofactors such as thiamine, coenzyme A, glutathione and the various enzymes that activate the substrates involved.

The rate of aerobic glycolysis, owing to operation of the Pasteur effect, is small in brain (46). Almost the entire energy for the brain's metabolic activities comes from oxidative breakdown of glucose. How far anaerobic energy, derived from glucose, may be important for some aspects of the activity of the nervous system is still unknown, but there is no reason as yet to regard it as significant except in the brain of the newborn. There is, however, the possibility that glycolysis is concerned with the regulation of pH with consequent effects on brain circulation (49). In this connection, too, it is well to point out that an enzyme that plays an important role in pH regulation, namely carbonic anhydrase, is present in brain in amounts that fluctuate in mental disorder (156). Whilst most of the glycolytic enzymes (499) are in the cytoplasm, it is claimed that about 10% of the glycolytic activity is associated with the brain mitochondria (498).

Aerobic glycolysis is greatly increased by respiratory inhibitors which impede the operation of the Pasteur effect. It is increased when cerebral activity occurs as in convulsions or *in vitro* after electrical stimulation or in presence of a high ratio of K^+/Ca^{++}. Some typical results are shown in Table 12 (41).

TABLE 12
RATE OF LACTIC ACID FORMATION IN BRAIN

	Animal	micromoles lactic acid/g/hour
In situ. normal	man	6
In situ, convulsing (92)	cat or dog	400
Brain cortex slices, normal (73)	man	25
Brain cortex slices electrical stimulated (73)	man	75
	rat	100-400

Although, as is well known, the presence of high concentrations of K^+ increases aerobic glycolysis (54,55), it inhibits anaerobic glycolysis, a phenomenon also brought about by application of electric impulses (41). The reason for the increased aerobic glycolysis by high K^+ is not known with certainty. It could be connected with the fact that K^+ catalyses the interaction of phosphopyruvate and ADP (157), but it may act (88) by increasing the ratio of $DPNH_2/DPN$ by an accelerating effect (in brain slices) on the reduction of DPN by pyruvate. (Increase of $DPNH_2/DPN$ will lead to an increased rate of lactate formation from pyruvate.) Increased K^+, however, as mentioned earlier, may increase glycolytic rates by stimulating formation of ADP and inorganic phosphate. Conceivably all these reactions may occur.

Just as a potassium-calcium antagonism occurs in the stimulation of brain respiration, it also occurs in the stimulation of anaerobic brain glycolysis but the effects are reversed. Some typical results are shown in Table 13 (130).

TABLE 13

EFFECTS OF POTASSIUM AND CALCIUM IONS ON ANAEROBIC GLYCOLYSIS

K^+	Ca^{++}	Anaerobic glycolysis of guinea pig brain cortex slices $Q_{CO_2}^{N_2}$
0	0	4.7
0	1 mM	11.9
4 mM	0	4.1
4 mM	1 mM	8.0

A powerful stimulator of brain anaerobic glycolysis is pyruvate, which restores the glycolysis of a calcium-free medium to the normal level (169). It should be pointed out that brain slices that have been exposed to nitrogen in the absence of glucose are incapable of anaerobic glycolysis unless they are re-exposed to oxygen before addition of glucose (130, 131). The effects of anaerobic deprivation of glucose are not apparent at 0°C. It is likely that the effect is concerned with the anaerobic destruction of ATP.

Turnover of Glucose in the Brain

Coxon (158) has shown that when radioactive glucose (glucose-C^{14}) is injected into an animal, the brain produces $C^{14}O_2$ very rapidly from the circulating blood glucose and concludes that brain has little reserve fuel and uses very rapidly the glucose submitted by the blood stream.

Geiger (60) has reported on the fate of glucose-U-C^{14} (uniformly labelled glucose) taken up by the brain in perfusion experiments from the circulating fluid. He has found that only 30-35% of the glucose taken up by the brain is oxidized directly under 'resting' conditions, another 20-30% of the glucose is rapidly transformed into acid soluble components containing amino acids and other amounts are built into the lipids. The amount of oxygen used by the brain closely corresponds with that necessary to take up all the glucose that has disappeared from the blood. These results as well as those of Allweis and Magnes (492) on oxygen uptake and glucose utilization may be explained on the basis of the facts given in Figure 1. The relatively large quantities of amino acids present in the brain transaminate with radioactive keto acids derived from glucose-U-C^{14}, so that, in effect, unlabelled α-ketonic acids are substituted for the radioactive ones and the glucose oxidation is accomplished in the normal way. Part of the radioactivity, instead of appearing in CO_2, is transferred to the brain amino acids and to the various metabolic reactions in which these are involved. The pooling of intermediates derived from glucose breakdown with brain cell constituents is obviously a normal aspect of brain cell chemistry. Geiger (60) has pointed out the important fact, as a result of his perfusion experiments, that the liver contributes substances, possibly uridine and cytidine, that are important for carbohydrate metabolism and the maintenance of brain function. Perhaps these are concerned with the maintenance of lipid structures in the nerve cells. Deficiency of these may be involved in the pathogenesis of hepatic coma.

NUTRITIONAL DEFICIENCIES AND DISEASES OF THE BRAIN

PELLAGRA

ALTHOUGH there is but little evidence that uncomplicated nicotinic acid (or amide) deficiency leads to injury in the nervous system (40), psychotic symptoms associated with pellagra are relieved by administration of nicotinic acid or its amide (41). Human requirements for dietary nicotinic acid are about 10 to 30 mg. per day. A proportion of the daily requirement of nicotinic acid is derived from the normal breakdown in the body of tryptophan. Pellagra is reported to be one of the causes of secondary illness in patients in mental hospitals, possibly due to faulty feeding habits and the difficulty in recognizing in them some of the mental changes characteristic of pellagra. The symptoms include depression, dizziness, insomnia and sometimes apprehension and hallucinations. Lehman (41) points out that the therapeutic effects of nicotinic acid administration in psychotic states, characterized by stupor, lethargy, coma or confusion, are not necessarily due to the correction of a nicotinic acid deficiency; possibly the large doses given have other effects on the nervous system. However, in an experiment in which nicotinamide was administered to a group of patients under close observation, the mental disturbances disappeared after administration and reappeared when the nicotinamide was no longer given (160). The therapeutic effect of nicotinamide was effective with pellagrins and not with subjects with similar symptoms due to alcoholism or schizophrenia. In the absence of nicotinamide treatment degenerative structural changes occur, particularly in the large neurons of the motor cortex, the brain stem and the anterior horn of the spinal cord.

The enzyme that splits DPN in brain (161), termed DPN-ase, may play a role in brain function of broader significance than may be expected from a simple hydrolytic system. Kaplan (162) has reported that the administration of 3-acetylpyridine, an anaoglue of nicotinamide in which the amino group is substituted by the methyl group, leads to severe lesions in the hypothalamus. The development of neural abnormalities by acetylpyridine may be prevented by administration of nicotinamide but not of nicotinic acid. This phenomenon is apparently due to the fact that acetylpyridine and nicotinamide can compete with each other for incorporation into DPN, the controlling enzyme, DPN-ase, acting as a transferase. Acetylpyridine is an antagonist of nicotinamide particularly in mice receiving diets deficient in nicotinamide. It has relatively little toxicity to newborn rats. The amount of DPN-ase in brain at birth is small and rises with age. Another nicotinamide analogue, 6-aminonicotinamide, also affects the nervous system, particularly the brain, as shown in experiments with developing chick embryo (163). There can be little doubt that interference with the pyridine nucleotide carrier system in the brain brings about a variety of nervous disturbances.

The importance of dietary tryptophan in preventing pellagra is, of course, well known. The disease occurs normally almost solely in people on diets deficient in both nicotinamide and tryptophan. It is remarkable that in some patients with the malignant carcinoid syndrome, symptoms of pellagra develop. This is possibly due to pre-emption of the dietary tryptophan by the tumour (229).

BERI-BERI

Patients deprived of thiamine show a variety of cerebral changes including depression, anxiety, irritability and loss of memory. If the deprivation is severe, serious disorders of the central nervous system take place which may be accompanied by the peripheral neuropathy characteristic of beri-beri. With prolonged deprivation of thiamine, neurological changes are the most prominent clinical features; an acute deficiency would be more accurately described as producing personality changes (40). These symptoms are relieved by administration of thiamine.

The following are values that have been reported (41):

Thiamine content in human brain cortex: normal 1.0 γ/g.; with increased thiamine in the diet 1.2 γ/g.; poor nutrition, high fever and vomiting 0.5 γ/g.; poor nutrition, alcoholism 0.6 γ/g. There can be little doubt from the clinical and biochemical evidence that the cerebral abnormalities due to thiamine deficiency are linked with the fact, already discussed, that diphosphothiamine is needed for glucose oxidation in the brain. In fact this phenomenon, the cerebral effects of thiamine deficiency (polyneuritis) in pigeons (64), was among the earliest to indicate the importance of carbohydrate metabolism for the normal functioning of the central nervous system. It is for this among other reasons that the enzymology of glucose breakdown must receive close attention in studies of cerebral dysfunction. According to von Muralt (457), thiamine is also intimately connected with conduction of impulses by peripheral nerve.

Both in patients with beri-beri, and in dogs with experimentally induced thiamine deficiency, the concentrations of pyruvic and lactic acids in the blood are found to vary directly with the severity of the disease.

The sites for pyruvic acid production seem to be the peripheral nerves, spinal cord, various parts of the brain stem, cerebellum and cerebral hemispheres. Correlation between degenerative changes in the central nervous system, clinical symptoms and biochemical abnormalities occurs not only in man but in dog and in the pigeon (40).

Wernicke's encephalopathy, characterized by clouding of consciousness, ataxia, and opthalmoplegia, with foci of nuclear degeneration and hemorrhage in the midbrain, and hypothalamic region of the brain stem, responds to treatment with thiamine. When the disease has progressed to the stage involving peripheral neuritis and changes in consciousness, irreversible damage in cerebral structures usually occurs. Thiamine administration may only be partly curative; there may remain considerable personality change, failure of memory and disorientation in time and space (Korsakoff syndrome).

The requirement for thiamine increases with increase of carbohydrate intake. In thiamine deficiency, a high carbohydrate diet may give rise to high blood levels of pyruvic acid and excess of this substance may bring about cerebral dysfunction. It is known that deficiency signs in animals are more severe on carbohydrate-containing than on carbohydrate-free diets, although the thiamine content in the brains of both groups of animals are the same (164).

Thiamine exists largely in the blood as the pyrophosphate which enters the brain, to judge from brain tissue experiments, more slowly than thiamine itself. Animal tissues contain a pyrophosphatase, which may aid in the transport of the vitamin to the brain where it is once more phosphorylated and can again play its role as cofactor in the metabolism of α ketonic acids. The content of thiamine varies in different parts of the brain, it being highest in cerebellum and basal ganglia and lowest in cortical white matter (41). Ochoa and Peters (165) showed that there is less thiamine than thiamine pyrophosphate in liver and brain and that there is a relatively larger increase in the pyrophosphate of brain than of other organs when vitamin deficient pigeons are dosed with thiamine.

A thiamine analogue, pyrithiamine, can produce the symptoms characteristic of thiamine deficiency and the disease may be prevented or cured by adding sufficient amounts of thiamine (166).

Consumption of raw fish, which contains an enzyme, thiaminase, that breaks down thiamine (164), gives rise to cerebral symptoms resembling those of Wernicke's syndrome including localized hemorrhagic brain lesions. This is an important matter in oriental countries where raw fish, or fish sauces in which thiaminase has not been destroyed, is consumed in abundance.

The concentrations of free keto acids tend to increase through the body with deprivation of thiamine and thus lead to relatively high levels in the blood stream especially after a carbohydrate meal. Favourable response to thiamine may not occur in all subjects who show neurological disorders and high blood levels of ketonic acids (167) and there is clearly much more still to be learned of the relationship between brain disorders and blood concentrations of ketonic acids.

FLAVIN DEFICIENCY

Riboflavin (vitamin B_2) deficiency gives rise, in man and experimental animals, to loss of physical activity and appetite followed by collapse and coma. Dogs deficient in this vitamin that plays a major role in cell respiration exhibit ultimately demyelination in peripheral nerves and in the spinal cord (168).

TRANSPORT PHENOMENA

BLOOD-BRAIN BARRIER

THE rate of metabolism of a metabolite, or a nutrient, in the cell may, under certain circumstances, be determined by its rate of entry into the cell. This is determined party by passive diffusion and partly by active transport, a subject of considerable study at the present time.

The penetration of many substances from the circulation to the neural tissues is limited drastically by what has come to be known as the blood-brain barrier. Its existence was first shown by Ehrlich in 1885 when he found that certain dyestuffs which stain most tissues are not taken up by the central nervous system. Trypan blue, an acid dye, was shown by Goldman to be a dye that stains only after intrathecal injection or following excessively high concentrations given intravenously. In this connection, it may be noted that dyes that have large inhibitory effects on muscle respiration have little or none, under the same experimental conditions, on brain respiration (170) presumably because the dye is unable to reach the site of the respiratory enzymes in the brain cells. Both *in vivo* and *in vitro* a barrier is presented by the brain cell membrane to a variety of substances that seem to have much easier access to the cell interior in most other tissues. Some substances, however, e.g. (bromophenol blue) that do not pass the blood brain barrier can penetrate deeply into nuclear regions from the ventricular cavities (491).

The fact that many substances fail to enter the cerebrospinal fluid and the nervous system led to the hypothesis that brain possesses a "protective" mechanism to which the name of blood-brain barrier was given. There is no complete impermeability to biologically important ions and molecules, but there is a diminished rate of entry compared with that in non-nervous tissues. Water (as shown by experiments with D_2O) enters rapidly.

41

Lipoid soluble substances generally pass easily through the capillary walls into the brain. Gases which are fairly soluble in lipids (e.g., oxygen) also pass through with apparent ease (173). Large molecules, such as albumin, do not penetrate at all. Anions such as chloride, bromide, iodide, thiocyanate, phosphate and borate which, outside the central nervous system, equilibrate in a few minutes across the capillary membrane do not reach equilibrium values in the brain in three hours (173,174). A steady state between plasma and cerebrospinal fluid sodium is not established before 21 hours after administration of isotopic sodium. Equilibration between plasma potassium and the brain is not complete even after 18 hours (178). There is little direct evidence that the important physiologically active amines, like the catecholamines, pass across the blood-brain barrier (438). However, it is to be emphasized that some special structures of the brain seem to lack the "protection" of the blood-brain barrier. This includes the pituitary gland and parts of the hypothalamus, the area postrema, the choroid plexus and the pineal gland (173).

Although the blood-barrier is primarily a physiological concept there has been much attempt to locate it anatomically. Various efforts in this direction have been discussed by Brierley (171) and by Bakay (173). Artefacts of technical procedure have led at times to serious misconceptions regarding both the site and nature of the barrier. It is now usually regarded as a function of the vascular endothelium, the perivascular glial membrane and (or) the interstitial ground substance. Richter (see 171) believes that its site is the layer of glial membranes enmeshed in mucoid material which apparently surrounds the cerebral capillaries. A study with fluorescent dyes led to the conclusion that the chief barrier to the entrance of the dyes lies "between the outer wall of the capillary endothelium and the glial plasma membrane," a space which is filled with amorphous ground substance (439).

The blood-brain barrier can largely be explained on the basis of the idea that the brain contains virtually no extracellular fluid and very little ground substance (441), glia and neurons being packed together in the greater part of it. Thus, to enter the brain, substances must pass through the cell membranes. Edstrom (441) has calculated that the area of brain cells exposed to the cerebrospinal fluid is in fact much larger than that exposed to blood *via* the pores in capillary walls, thus explaining the relative rapidity with which substances penetrate into the brain when injected into the cerebrospinal fluid. However, the conclusion that there is little extracellular fluid present in the cerebral cortex (5-7%) is based on studies made with the electron microscope and disagree with a number of other observations on the cortex (442). For example, measurements of the electrical impedance of the cortex suggest a volume of interstitial fluid amounting to 27-35%. It is possible that there are, in the cortex, glia cells with ion permeable, and, therefore, low resistance membranes. Such structures would have the value of an extracellular fluid in impedance measurements. The existence of such cells, however, is still hypothetical.

Krogh (172), in a survey of exchange through the surfaces of living cells, has concluded that the permeability of blood vessels differs materially from that in other organs. It has been postulated, however (440), that the apparent differences between the permeabilities of capillaries in brain and those in other tissues may be due to active transport of substances by the neuroglia. The lack of widespread diffusion of dyes through the brain after the perivascular barrier has been broken by wounds suggests that another factor, possibly the neuroglia, limits diffusion through the brain substance (439).

Pentavalent arsenic compounds such as tryparsamide can penetrate the brain; for they not only enter the cerebrospinal fluid readily but they also achieve greater trypanocidal activity there than the trivalent arsenicals (192). It is pointed out that the level of trypanocidal activity in cerebrospinal fluid has little relation to the total arsenic content because the maximum cerebrospinal fluid level of total arsenic is reached at or before 14 hours after parenteral administration whereas the maximum trypanocidal activity occurs only after 30-40 hours. These results are held to indicate that the pentavalent arsenic compound penetrates the blood-brain barrier and becomes reduced (by glutathione) in the brain to the trypanocidally active trivalent arsenic derivative which passes into the cerebrospinal fluid. The access of parenterally given trivalent arsenic compounds is hindered by formation of protein complexes in the plasma. Possibly bismuth may behave in an analogous manner (193).

The lipid soluble narcotics, ether, chloroform, as well as alcohol and a number of barbiturates penetrate with relative ease into the central nervous system (for discussion, see Harris, 194).

Much work has been carried out on the penetration of antibiotics into the brain and this is discussed by Holmes and Tower (195). Most sulfonamides have been found to penetrate readily into the brain from the blood. After parenteral doses of penicillin, therapeutic effective levels are found in the cerebrospinal fluid in 2-4 hours. In the absence of meningeal involvement, little if any streptomycin reaches the cerebrospinal fluid from the blood. In tuberculous meningitis the amount of streptomycin in the cerebrospinal fluid varies with the severity of the disease; increasing amounts are found with clinical deterioration, less as the condition improves. Other antibiotics such as chlortetracycline and chloramphenicol are able to penetrate into the central nervous system.

Waelsch (179) points out that whereas glutamine readily enters the central nervous system from the blood, glutamate apparently is not taken up by the brain *in vivo*. In the newborn rat, intraperitoneal injection of glutamate leads to increased brain glutamate levels (180) but ten days after birth this effect disappears and no net uptake of glutamate appears. Nevertheless, isotopic tracer studies show that glutamate from the plasma exchanges with brain glutamate, with no change in cerebral level of the amino acid (181). The fact that exchange diffusion may occur much more rapidly than the process of active transfer is now well established (182). Labelled lysine, it may be noted, is taken up (by exchange) at a relatively rapid rate from the circulating blood by the brain of an adult mouse (186).

The results of experiments of Kamin and Handler (211) in which amino acids were given intravenously at a constant rate into lightly anaesthetized dogs are shown in Table 14. They show that certain amino acids, if not glutamic and aspartic acids, can add to their quotas in brain if present in blood at relatively high concentrations.

Amino acids enter the brain rapidly by the intrathecal route (183) and methionine, when introduced directly into the cerebrospinal fluid by intracisternal or subarachnoid injection, is incorporated into the brain proteins (184).

TABLE 14

PERMEABILITY OF BRAIN TISSUE TO AMINO ACIDS(211)

Amino Acid	Plasma Increment over control in μmoles/g. tissue	Brain Increment over control in μmoles/g. tissue
Glutamic	23 - 60	0
Aspartic	27 - 40	0
Methionine	15; 17	4; 2
Histidine	58; 50	6; 7
Lysine	70; 51	3; 9
Arginine	21; 25	2; 1

Although glucose is taken up by the brain, fructose is taken up very much more slowly (187) and sucrose only in minute quantities. Within 3 hours following intravenous injection of 100 to 200 ml. 50% sucrose in men, no sucrose or only a very small amount, is recovered from the brain (173). In this connection, it should be pointed out that the sugars may interfere with each others' transport into the brain cell. Thus the presence of glucose almost completely inhibits the production of $C^{14}O_2$ from uniformly labelled fructose-C^{14} in presence of rat brain cortex slices (87). Fructose, in fact, is not oxidized to CO_2 (or only to a very small extent) in the presence of glucose. So complete a suppression of fructose oxidation makes it seem possible that glucose interferes with the transport of fructose, though doubtless the major effect is due to an inhibition of fructose phosphorylation by glucose phosphate esters.

Phosphate is taken up by the brain, but the rate of uptake in the brain of the newborn and immature animal is very rapid compared with that of the adult. The slowness of uptake of phosphate by the brain from the blood is shown by the fact that, using radioactive phosphate, the relative specific activity of the ATP (ratio of radioactive phosphate in the labile groups of ATP to that in the inorganic phosphate) is only about 40% after one hour. A much higher figure is obtained if the labelled phosphate is injected intracranially (188).

ACTIVE TRANSPORT

It is now well known that sugars, amino acids, inorganic ions, even water may undergo active transport into cells (123), that is to say, transport against a diffusion gradient. Energy derived from

TABLE 15

DISTRIBUTION OF ELECTROLYTES IN BRAIN, PLASMA
AND CEREBROSPINAL FLUID

Constituent	Brain	meq./1. Plasma	Cerebrospinal fluid
Na^+	57	141	141
K^+	96	5	2.5
Ca^{++}	2	2.5	1.5
Mg^{++}	11	1.9	1.2
Cl^-	37	109	127
HCO_3^-	12	27	18
Phosphate	16	2	1

respiration, and sometimes from glycolysis, is essential for such transport.

Values of the concentrations of constituents in the human brain, blood plasma and cerebrospinal fluid are given in Table 15 (41,175). The differences between the steady state levels shown in this table are presumably ultimately due to metabolic events taking place in the brain.

According to current theory (443) the movements of ions across surface membranes of cells occur by two mechanisms, one by which ions move freely by diffusion and the other by which they move against their electrochemical gradient, a process requiring energy ultimately derived from metabolism. A knowledge of the details of these processes is fundamental to an understanding of electrophysiological events. These processes seem to be similar in many varieties of cells. The relationship between ionic movements at the brain cell surface and the energetics involved has already been briefly discussed. The reader is referred, for further discussion of the physical chemistry of ion transport, to the articles of Ussing (444), Eccles (443), Teorell (445), Hodgkin (446). Several workers (508, 509) have suggested that phosphatides, including phosphatidic acid, may be cation carriers at the nerve cell membrane and Hokin and Hokin (508) have suggested a cycle of events, enzyme controlled (and including a phosphorylation step) to account for sodium transport.

The distribution of electrolytes in brain *in vitro* is partly determined by the presence of glutamate. When brain cortex slices containing approx. 100 meq./l. K^+ are placed in a normal Ringer medium (containing 5 meq./l. K^+) they gradually lose potassium, even in the presence of oxygen. If glucose is present in the medium the loss of K^+ is greatly reduced, and if both glucose and glutamate are present the leakage of potassium is stopped (176). Potassium ions can be assimilated in brain cortex slices at 60 μmoles/g./hr. and can exchange with potassium ions in the surrounding medium at 180 μmoles/g./hr. These, of course, are values obtained with isolated brain cortex slices in which the "blood-brain barrier" is absent. Nevertheless, it is possible to obtain data with such tissues concerning transport into the brain cell from the surrounding medium which may be of value in the understanding of the mechanism of the blood-brain barrier. Active transport of gluta-mate* also occurs, for accumulation of this substance in brain cortex slices against a concentration gradient takes place so long as there is oxidative metabolism taking place in presence of glucose.

The ionic composition of the incubation medium greatly affects the uptake of both glutamate and K^+ in brain cortex slices. The presence of sodium ions is indispensable (185). Calcium ions affect differently the transport of potassium and glutamate, in-dicating, as might be anticipated, that the mechanisms involved are also different.

BRAIN TUMOURS

Brain tumours stain selectively with dyes such as Nile Blue and fluorescein which have been used for location of the tumors (190). Sucrose permeates into many tumours (including glioblastomas, astrocytomas, meningiomas) with little or no penetration into the brain substance. Again, radioactive phosphate injected intra-venously appears in high concentration when compared with normal brain. Other substances, that can be detected by use of their radioactive isotopes, which penetrate at a higher rate into brain tumours than into the brain substance, are potassium, manganese, copper, arsenic, iodinated human serum albumin, sodium iodide (see Bakay, 173, 191 for discussion).

A method of therapy for glioblastoma multiforme, as yet in the experimental stage, depends on the non-specific penetration of borate into the tumour. B^{10}, a stable isotope of boron, is rendered radioactive by irradiation with low energy neutrons which have little direct effect on tissue. In this manner ionizing radiations are brought to bear on the tumour from within the tumour itself (447)

*Uptakes of glycine (524) and γaminobutyric acid (518), against a concentration gradient, also occur.

BRAIN INJURIES

Brain injuries greatly affect the blood-brain barrier. This was known from early investigations on permeability of dyes in experimental or pathological injuries to the brain. Permeability changes (173) follow simple exposure of the cortex, touching the surface of the brain with hydrogen peroxide, or even pressing the brain. It seems that the duration of the breakdown of the blood-brain barrier, as studied by the permeation of vital dyes (trypan blue, fluorescein) is proportional to the severity of the damage. It is believed that the vital staining of the injured areas of the brain is due to escape of the dye through the capillary walls.

Radioactive phosphate penetration into the brain is increased in the brains of cats with traumatic and ischemic lesions (189). Bakay (173) has shown that in the lesions, and areas of necrosis, following injury to the brain, there is greatly increased permeability of phosphate from the blood and considers the use of labelled phosphate as more sensitive than that of vital dyes for following the effects of injuries to the brain.

Cerebral lesions caused by air emboli, intracerebral hematomas, and lesions due to infections similarly result in changes in the blood-brain barrier.

CEREBRAL OEDEMA

Brain swelling takes place in cerebral concussion and, as observed by Cannon (198) reduced cerebral blood flow occurs with rise of intracranial pressure. Anoxia in the brain results in an increased fluid content both intracellular and extracellular (196). A marked increase in electrical impedance takes place in the cortex. This is apparently connected with a shift of extracellular electrolytes (mainly NaCl) into cellular elements in the cortex, accompanied by water transfer (442). This is in accord with the *in vitro* evidence that aerobic respiration of brain is essential for normal ionic distributions.

Brain cortex slices suspended in a Ringer medium containing glucose swell rapidly under anaerobic conditions (137), but, even when provided with oxygen some swelling occurs (less than that anaerobically) amounting to an increase in weight of about 16% in 20 minutes (199).

It seems likely that cerebral oedema as observed clinically, following trauma to the brain, corresponds to the phenomena seen *in vitro*.

It is considered wise to irrigate brain with fluid approximating in composition to cerebrospinal fluid in order to minimize fluid and electrolyte shifts (197).

LEAD AND TIN POISONING

It is now well known that cerebral oedema can be induced by lead poisoning and by poisoning with organic tin compounds.

Many industrial poisons have generalized effects which may include effects on the nervous system (200). The consequences of lead poisoning, however, seem to be more directly connected with the brain itself as they include epileptiform convulsions, paralysis, headache, delirium, and mania. Many explanations have been offered, such as cerebral arteritis, arteriosclerosis or anemia; a direct action of lead on cortical cells; meningeal lesions, or even indirect effects from kidney dysfunction or disturbed porphyrin metabolism. Although localized lesions such as minute hemorrhages and cellular infiltrations have been found in the brains of patients who have died of lead encephalopathy it is possible to attribute the symptoms to the increased intracranial tension due to intense cerebral oedema. This is particularly obvious when the effects of lead on the early morphogenesis of the chick are studied; one observes changes that range from small herniation of the meninges to frank hydrocephalus.

In patients a peripheral neuropathy, often purely motor, may occur and is most usually seen in adults; the severe encephalopathy with convulsions and focal signs often occurs in children.

The exact biochemical mechanisms involved in lead toxicity are not known but it is evident that a reversible system is set up, as modern treatment with a chelating agent such as calcium disodium salt of ethylenediamine tetracetic acid (Versene) appears to be effective.

When rats are fed on a diet containing triethyl tin they develop an interstitial oedema in the central nervous system (201) and this is apparently the only abnormality, except for testicular atrophy, found after long exposure to the poison. The neurological disturbances due to triethyl tin (202) are probably associated with the fact (203) that administration of triethyl tin to brain preparations *in vitro* brings about, at low concentrations, an uncoupling of phosphorylation from oxidation and an inhibition of phosphate uptake in liver mitochondria which are oxidizing a variety of substrates. Further work (204) has made it clear that the oxidative metabolism of brain slices is very strongly affected by low concentrations of triethyl tin. Slices of brains, taken from the poisoned animals, give a metabolic picture similar to that found when triethyl tin is added *in vitro*.

Tetraethyl lead, manufactured primarily for inclusion in motor fuels, has highly toxic effects on the nervous system, of which acute mental changes are the most obvious manifestation. Histopathological changes have been demonstrated in the brains of man and laboratory animals (205). They may be brought about by inhalation of the substance or even by absorption through the skin.

Now, although small quantities of lead salts lead to severe hydrocephalus in the developing chick (206), as little as 0.075 mg. lead nitrate per yolk sac being effective, there is but little effect of small concentrations of lead salts on the respiratory activities of rat brain cortex slices in a glucose-Ringer medium. This led to the view that possibly neurological toxicity of lead *in vivo* may be partly due to the formation of lead organic complexes which are capable of affecting metabolism in the nervous system. Studies (206) with lead tetraethyl have shown that whilst this substance has little or no effect on the respiration of rat brain cortex slices in a glucose-Ringer medium, it brings about, at small concentrations (0.03 mM), marked inhibition of transport of glutamate into the brain cells. The effect is probably not confined to glutamate, for it occurs with at least one other amino acid tested (glycine). The effect, moreover, does not apply to all tissues, for lead tetraethyl at low concentrations has no effect on the transport of amino acids into tumour cells which are well known to concentrate them avidly. Tin tetraethyl, which also exerts neurological effects *in vivo*, behaves similarly to lead tetraethyl (Table 16) though it is quantitatively not so effective.

Whilst it is true that these effects of lead tetraethyl and tin tetraethyl have been observed on brain cortex slices, which lack the blood-brain barrier, they indicate the possibility that these

TABLE 16

Comparison of Effects of Lead Tetraethyl and Tin Tetraethyl on Radioactive Glutamate Uptake into Rat Brain Cortex Slices

Additions to glutamate-glucose-Ringer medium	Glutamate uptake in the slices after 1 hr. c/min./mg. dry weight
Nil	158
+ Lead tetraethyl 0.03 mM	55
0.06 mM	43
+ Tin tetraethyl 0.03 mM	113
0.1 mM	58

metallo-organic neurological poisons may exert their effects by disturbance of metabolic equilibria in the brain cell. The mechanism by which these poisons bring about the inhibition of glutamate (and other amino acid) transport into the brain cell is still unknown.

It is likely that the study of transport phenomena in the brain will clarify the modes of action of drugs affecting the nervous system. Thus competition of a structural analogue with a metabolite for active transport may prove to have considerable importance in brain function. A recent example is the competition of the hemicholiniums, a series of quarternary bases containing choline moieties, with choline for transport into the neuron, resulting in diminution of acetylcholine synthesis and thus in neuromuscular and ganglionic block (207). This has been demonstrated in brain slices *in vitro* and in perfused ganglia *in situ*.

EFFECTS OF CONVULSIONS

Increased permeability to the blood-brain barrier is said to occur following convulsions due to insulin, metrazol or electric current (208). The electrolyte balance is affected both in hypoglycemia (209) and in convulsive therapies (208), for the brain cells lose potassium and gain sodium. As Himwich points out (210), the convulsive therapies used in the treatment of certain forms of mental disorder, and hypoglycemic shock have much in common, though neurologically they differ markedly. The oxidative mechanism is apparently unable to support the increased cerebral excitement in convulsive therapy and anaerobic mechanisms to supply energy have to operate. With hypoglycemia, the brain cell is deprived of glucose; with metrazol or electroshock, the availability of glucose or oxygen is insufficient to meet the demand. How these mechanisms operate for therapy is unknown, but it is evident that the course and speed of metabolic events in the brain cells are greatly changed, with effects that are still the subject of many biochemical investigations. Peters and Tower (513), for example, point out that the metabolism of cat cerebral cortex slices after seizures due to methionine sulfoximine differs from the normal in showing diminished abilities to form glutamic acid, glutamine and γ-aminobutyric acid.

AMINO ACID METABOLISM IN THE BRAIN

AMINO ACID FORMATION

THE total free amino acid nitrogen in brain (cat) amounts to approximately 40 mg./100 g. compared with 6.4 mg./100 ml. in blood plasma. A group of amino acids, *viz.* glutamic acid, glutamine, γ-aminobutyric acid, aspartic acid and N-acetyl-aspartic acid, make up about 75% of the total free amino acids. The relative quantities of the amino acids in cat brain are given by the following values, expressed in micromoles per gram tissue (212): aspartic acid 2.2; asparagine 0.1; acetylaspartic acid 6.0; glutamic acid 8.7; glutamine 3.4; glycine 1.3; alanine 1.0; γ-aminobutyric acid 2.3; proline 0.14; cysteine 0.04; serine 0.72; glutathione 0.9; taurine 2.0. Whilst the amounts of amino acids "essential" for growth are present in small quantities, in concentrations approximating to those in the plasma, threonine and most of the "non-essential" amino acids are present in brain in considerably higher concentrations than in the plasma. Doubtless many of these are actively transported into brain, against the concentration gradient, and retained there so long as energy from respiration is made available.

Possibly one of the most striking features of the amino acid pattern in brain is the prominence of glutamic acid. About 2% of the wet weight of brain is nitrogen and of this 10–20% is non-protein nitrogen. About half of this consists of free amino acids and of this approximately half again is glutamic acid and glutamine.

The brain cell concentration of glutamate is probably maintained at its high level, under normal conditions, by the metabolism of glucose. Waelsch (213) has reported that incubated slices of brain cortex which have been depleted of glutamate are able to restore their glutamate concentration when glucose is supplied as sole substrate.

Possibly the most convincing evidence of the role of glucose in the maintenance of brain cell levels of the "non-essential" amino acids comes from studies with radioactive glucose.

It is now well known that when radioactive glucose is metabolized by brain cortex *in vitro* radioactive amino acids are formed. A mince of the brain of one day old mice when incubated with glucose uniformly labelled with C^{14} (i.e., glucose-U-C^{14}) incorporates radioactivity in all amino acids of brain protein with the exception of threonine (214). Rat brain cortex slices can convert glucose-C^{14} into labelled glutamic, aspartic and γ-aminobutyric acids (215). It is evident that glucose during its normal metabolism in the brain cell produces intermediates, the α-ketonic acids (see Fig. 1), that undergo conversion to amino acids largely at the expense of organic nitrogen already available in the brain cell. In these reactions, transaminations play a major role and by reason of these reactions amino acid interconversions take place. The amino acids play a vital role in brain function, not only for the maintenance of ionic balance in the cell but because they give rise to amines that are physiologically active and because they take part in the biosynthetic changes that maintain the structure of the cell.

Experiment (88) shows that a not inconsiderable fraction, possibly amounting to 10%, of glucose is converted into amino acids. Typical experimental results are shown in Table 17.

TABLE 17

FORMATION OF LABELLED AMINO ACIDS FROM 5mM GLUCOSE-U-C^{14} AND 5mM FRUCTOSE-U-C^{14} IN PRESENCE OF RAT BRAIN CORTEX SLICES AND EFFECTS OF K^+ (88) INCUBATION TIME = 1 HR.

Values expressed as counts/minute/100 mg. wet tissue

Amino acid formed	Glucose-U-C^{14} Initially 10^6 c/min.		Fructose-U-C^{14} Initially 10^6 c/min.	
	5 meq./1 K^+	105 meq./1 K^+	5 meq./1 K^+	105 meq./1 K^+
Glutamic acid	5057	5516	4784	942
Glutamine	1289	2397		
γ Aminobutyric acid	966	1491	739	271
Alanine	657	794	374	224
Aspartic acid	1318	1183	2159	2127

In a normal Ringer medium, there is a labelling of glutamic acid, glutamine, γ-aminobutyric acid, aspartic acid and alanine in the presence of glucose-U-C^{14} and of fructose-U-C^{14}. The labelling of glutamic acid, with both sugars, is highest among the amino acids investigated, aspartic acid showing the next highest activity. It may be noted that the ratios of radioactive glutamate, glutamine, and γ-aminobutyrate found with rat brain cortex in presence of glucose-U-C^{14} (and of increased potassium ions to stimulate respiration to the level found *in vivo*) are 1:0.44:0.27 which approximate to the ratios of these amino acids normally found in adult rat brain cortex (216) namely 1:0.43:0.17. It is noteworthy also that the labelling of aspartic acid, on incubation with fructose-U-C^{14} greatly exceeds that found after incubation with glucose-U-C^{14}.

It is evident from Figure 1 that labelled pyruvate, derived from glucose-U-C^{14} may transaminate with existing glutamic acid to give rise to labelled alanine and α-ketoglutaric acid (thus short-circuiting the citric acid cycle) which is metabolized in the normal way. Thus the labelled pyruvate may undergo a variety of re-actions that will yield all the labelled amino acids mentioned in Table 17. The glutamic acid in the cell is maintained, however, because the labelled amino acids in their turn transaminate with the unlabelled α-ketoglutarate to reform unlabelled glutamate. Thus a complex series of reactions takes place resulting ultimately in a steady-state, the net effect of which is the conversion of glu-cose to carbon dioxide and water. There will be no *net* synthesis of amino acids, for nitrogen is not added to the system, but a redistribution of the existing amino acids, which will all be in dynamic equilibrium. With fructose, as seen in Table 17, the steady-state of the amino acids at any given time will differ from that obtaining with glucose. Moreover the steady-state will vary with the electrolyte balance in the medium bathing the brain cortex slices and with the respiratory conditions. The distribution of the amino acids (e.g., as given in Table 17) may be explained on the conclusions that the main respiratory path of glucose lies along the citric acid cycle, that transaminations are largely respon-sible for the formation of the amino acids and that the effects of increased K$^+$ is to stimulate the citric acid cycle and particularly the rate of conversion of pyruvate to acetyl-CoA. Such stimulation may be indirect, as explained earlier. With such an interpretation, it is possible to understand the larger yield of labelled aspartate from fructose-U-C^{14} than from glucose-U-C^{14} because fructose is less able than glucose to yield sufficient pyruvate and, therefore, acetyl-CoA to remove oxalacetate as citrate. More oxalacetate is therefore transaminated to aspartate. The reader is referred to the publication of Kini and Quastel (88) for further details concerning carbohydrate-amino acid interrelations in brain cortex *in vitro*.

INTERCONVERSION OF AMINO ACIDS IN THE BRAIN

It is clear from Fig. 1 that interconversion of several amino acids is possible through the joint operation of the citric acid cycle and transaminase systems.

Recently it has been shown (217) that, in the rat, the brain can convert L-proline to glutamic acid, aspartic acid, alanine, arginine, γ-aminobutyric acid and ornithine. The penetration rate of proline ethyl ester greatly exceeds that of proline which is only poorly transported across the blood-brain barrier. Proline ethyl ester, once it has penetrated into the brain, is hydrolyzed to yield free proline. It appears (217, 517) that brain, like liver, can build arginine from ornithine, ammonia and carbon dioxide and that brain can also break down arginine to urea (517).

AMINO ACID OXIDATION

How far and in what way amino acids in the brain are implicated in its respiratory mechanisms is a problem under active investigation at the present day. Glutamic acid must play a prominent role for it inhibits anaerobic glycolysis (218), and accelerates aerobic glycolysis (219) in brain. Whilst it is conceivable that the inhibitory effect on glycolysis by glutamic acid is due to removal of keto acids by transamination (Fig. 1), the reason for the stimulation of aerobic glycolysis (i.e., inhibition of the Pasteur effect) is not clear. D-glutamate is even more effective than L-glutamate (185) in increasing aerobic glycolysis of brain, but neither form of the amino acid has any effect if potassium ions are omitted from the medium surrounding the brain slices. D-glutamate, when present with glucose, causes the accumulation of K^+ in brain slices but it is less effective than L-glutamate. It has been suggested (137) that the D-form of glutamate may be converted to the L-form in brain slices by deamination and reamination. It should also be borne in mind that D-glutamate may inhibit, by competition, metabolism of L-glutamate, as it, like α-methylglutamate, inhibits glutaminase (218,220). Thus D-glutamate may affect the normal equilibria in the brain cell between α keto acids and L-glutamate. There seems to be little doubt, however, that the effects of glutamate are linked with electrolyte balance and evidently it is not possible to understand the interactions of an amino acid, like glutamic acid, in glucose metabolism without knowing something of the influence of the amino acids on electrolyte balance and transaminase systems.

The fact that glutamic acid is oxidized by brain was shown nearly thirty years ago (63) and it was thought at one time to be the only amino acid capable of being oxidised (221).

Glutamic acid oxidation in the brain is DPN dependent, proceeding according to the reaction (222):

$$\text{Glutamic acid} + \text{DPN} \rightleftharpoons \alpha\text{-iminoglutaric acid} + \text{DPNH}_2$$

The equilibrium point is far to the left, and may only be attained if the hydrolysis of α-iminoglutaric acid is prevented.

$$\alpha\text{-iminoglutaric acid} + \text{H}_2\text{O} \rightleftharpoons \alpha \text{ ketoglutaric acid} + \text{NH}_3$$

The iminoglutaric acid is apparently stabilized by ammonia; so in the respiring brain cell, at a steady-state, the addition of ammonium ions will lead automatically to the formation of glutamate.

Respiration of brain slices in presence of L-glutamate is not as responsive to electric impulses as it is in presence of glucose, but according to McIlwain (73) human brain tissue, which consumes glutamate at a relatively vigorous rate, is responsive to the application of electric impulses in presence of the amino acid. The addition of potassium ions can stimulate the aerobic metabolism of L-glutamate in presence of rat brain cortex slices though the effect is not large except in presence of glucose (87). This can be seen in the values quoted in Table 18, where glutamate containing a labelled carboxyl group was used.

TABLE 18

Effects of 100 mM KCl on the Aerobic Metabolism of L-glutamate (Using Glutamic Acid-1-C^{14}) by Rat Brain Cortex Slices in 90 Minutes Initial Activity 10^5 c/min.

	L-glutamate-1-C^{14} 10 mM		L-glutamate-1-C^{14} + glucose 10 mM 10 mM	
	5 mM KCl	105 mM KCl	5 mM KCl	105 mM KCl
Oxygen consumed cmm./10 mg. dry weight tissue	216	278	186	340
C^{14}O$_2$ formed c/min./mg. dry weight	1450	1930	763	1560

According to Takagaki *et al.* (185) D-glutamate not only inhibits brain endogenous respiration (in absence of glucose) but also brain respiration in presence of L-glutamate. This result favours the conclusion that the endogenous respiration of brain *in vitro* takes place partly at the expense of the L-glutamate present.

γ-Aminobutyric Acid

This amino acid, found normally in the brain and derived from glutamic acid by decarboxylation, is oxidized in the brain cell (in the mitochondria), its oxidation being accompanied by phosphorylation in a manner similar to that occurring with glucose or L-glutamate (223). It is known (224) that, in brain tissue, γ-aminobutyrate transaminates with α-ketoglutarate, thus:

$$NH_2.CH_2CH_2.CH_2COOH + COOH.CH_2. CH_2CO.COOH =$$
$$CHO.CH_2.CH_2.COOH + COOH.CH_2CH_2.CHNH_2.COOH.$$

The succinic semialdehyde can be oxidized further to succinic acid by a DPN dependent enzyme (231) and oxidation thence proceeds normally through the citric acid cycle. Evidence for this comes from experiments with labelled γ-aminobutyric acid given to mice (225) or added to brain slices (226) and homogenates (227). It seems definite that the oxidation of γ-aminobutyric acid proceeds through succinic acid after the preliminary transamination and aldehyde oxidation.

γ-Aminobutyric acid can also react with arginine in presence of brain to form γ-guanidinobutyric acid (228) which is a normal constituent of brain.

The formation of labelled γ-aminobutyric acid from labelled glucose is shown in Table 17 and indicates that this amino acid, like glutamic acid and aspartic acid, takes part in the dynamic equilibrium states characterizing the brain cell.

Glycine

Glycine is decomposed in rat brain cortex slices to yield carbon dioxide. This process, in which $C^{14}O_2$ is formed from carboxyl labelled glycine, is markedly stimulated by the presence of glucose, the rate of production of carbon dioxide being increased at least three fold (65). The manner in which this metabolism of glycine takes place in brain is still uncertain. Quantitatively, it is small compared with that of glutamic acid.

Trytophan and 5-Hydroxytryptophan

These amino acids, important in the brain as precursors of serotonin (5-hydroxy-indolethylamine), pass readily from the blood stream into the brain, but whether tryptophan is oxidized to hydroxytryptophane in the brain is still not known. The latter amino acid has not been detected in the brain, possibly because it is metabolized (by decarboxylation) so rapidly. It apparently penetrates most easily into those areas of the brain which are rich in its decarboxylase and where serotonin is normally found (230).

AMINO ACID DECARBOXYLATION

Brain decarboxylases, that convert α amino acids to the corresponding amines, are assuming considerable importance in view of the possible physiological activities of these amines in brain function.

Decarboxylation of the parent amino acids to the amines take place in the nervous system probably at the sites where the amines operate. This conclusion seems to follow from the fact that amines are much more poorly transported into the brain from the circulation than the corresponding amino acids. Moreover amines formed elsewhere in the body, or introduced into the body, are likely to be broken down by amine oxidase in the liver. It seems likely, therefore, that brain decarboxylations are necessary for the formation of biologically active amines *in situ*.

Brain tissue is rich in a decarboxylase which converts L-glutamic acid into γ-aminobutyric acid (232). The decarboxylase, like the amino acid transaminases, is pyridoxal phosphate (vitamin B_6) dependent.

The physiological interest in γ-aminobutyric acid lies in the fact that it, or a substance to which it gives rise, may be an inhibitory transmitter. Florey (233) found that extracts of the mammalian brain inhibit spontaneous activity of, and blocks the effect of acetylcholine on, the stretch receptor neuron of the cray fish. The responsible substance in the extract seemed to be γ-aminobutyric acid (234). At about the same time Hayashi *et al.* (235) reported that γ-aminobutyric acid and related compounds, especially γ-amino-β-hydroxybutyric acid, can inhibit convulsions induced in dogs by electrical or chemical means. Later work (see 236 for discussion) made clear the important neurophysiological activity of γ-aminobutyric acid.

The tissues of the central nervous system are distinguished from other tissues, in a large variety of animals, by the presence of γ-aminobutyric acid. Doubtless it plays a significant role in brain function.

The decarboxylase acting on 5-hydroxytryptophan to liberate serotonin is found localized in the brain stem particularly in the hypothalamus and midbrain. Usually the serotonin is found at the site of the decarboxylase. If brain serotonin is increased by administration of 5-hydroxytryptophan, there follows central excitation, like that observed on electrical stimulation of the areas in the brain which regulate behavioural and autonomic functions (230). Only the L-isomer of 5-hydroxytryptophan increases brain serotonin levels and only the L-isomer has pharmacological effects. Costa and Himwich (237) point out that insulin convulsions cause changes in serotonin concentrations in various parts of the brain and that hydroxytryptophan decarboxylase activity is reduced as a result of insulin injections.

Tryptophan decarboxylation can also occur in brain, giving rise to tryptamine (indolethylamine) which has been found to be normally present. Tryptophan itself occurs in the brains of most animals (504) in concentrations of about 1-3 γ/g tissue, about 3-10 times the corresponding concentration of serotonin. The richest sources of tryptophan are the pons and hypothalamus.

Adrenaline and noradrenaline occur in the nervous system. It seems very likely that noradrenaline is formed in the neuron itself (238), but its irregular distribution in the nerve cell has given rise to the view that the presence of specialized structures is necessary for its formation. It is claimed (239) that noradrenaline is formed by the introduction of a hydroxyl group into hydroxytyramine which is formed from dihydroxyphenylalanine (DOPA) by a decarboxylase (240). Presumably this enzyme must be present in the nervous system. The noradrenaline content of the brain is low and may perhaps be derived from the vasomotor nerves. It is present in the hypothalamus. Vogt (241) finds that there is a pattern of distribution of noradrenaline in different parts of the brain suggesting that part of the cerebral noradrenaline is not in the adrenergic vasomotor fibres. It is not found in myelinated fibres but in special regions of grey matter consisting of neurons, glia and non-myelinated fibres. Small quantities of adrenaline usually accompany noradrenaline in brain.

The current active interest in the catecholamines, as substances connected with manifestations of mental disorder, will doubtless stimulate many more investigations on the enzymology of catecholamine formation in the brain.

PYRIDOXINE

Vitamin B_6 (pyridoxine) plays so important a role as a cofactor (as pyridoxal phosphate, which is synthesized in brain from pyridoxal and ATP) in various aspects of nitrogen metabolism, that a deficiency of it in the body, either by absence from the diet or by inactivation by chemical reagents introduced into the body, may well have dire consequences to health. The coenzyme is known to be essential for transamination reactions, for amino acid decarboxylase systems, and for the active transport of amino acids into the living cell. Braunstein (242), who drew attention in 1937-39 to the biological importance of transaminations (243), claims pyridoxal catalyzed reactions as a basis of nitrogen metabolism and there is much to support this point of view. In a variety of aspects of amino acid metabolism, α-ketoglutarate plays a key role, for this substance is one of the most effective molecules for transaminations and is an important constituent of the citric acid cycle (Fig. 1). In addition, the coenzyme is involved in various aspects of tryptophan metabolism (e.g., nicotinic acid formation), in the condensation between glycine and succinyl-CoA (Fig. 1) to produce heme and the porphyrins, and in the building of a sphingosine precursor from serine and a fatty-acyl derivative.

The list of reactions given in Table 19, compiled by Hoare and Snell (244), shows the scope of reactions catalyzed by pyridoxal. It is possible that metal ions (e.g. zinc) may be involved in these reactions.

The mechanism of action of pyridoxal may be found in the reversible non-enzymatic reactions of pyridoxal and amino acids (245) e.g.:

Pyridoxal + amino acid   (A) $\leftrightarrows$ Pyridoxamine + keto acid (A)
Pyridoxamine + keto acid (B) $\leftrightarrows$ Pyridoxal + amino acid   (B)

TABLE 19

Type of Biological Reactions Catalyzed by Pyridoxal

Racemisation	$\text{R. } \overset{\text{H}}{\underset{\text{NH}_2}{\text{C.COOH}}} \leftrightarrows \text{R.} \overset{\text{NH}_2}{\underset{\text{H}}{\text{C.COOH}}}$
Transamination	$\text{R'CHNH}_2\text{COOH} + \text{R''CO.COOH}$ $\leftrightarrows \text{R'COCOOH} + \text{R''CHNH}_2 \text{ COOH}$
Aldol reactions	$\text{R.CHOH.CHNH}_2\text{.COOH} \leftrightarrows \text{R.CHO} + \text{NH}_2.\text{CH}_2.\text{COOH}$
Dehydration $\big\}$ Deamination	$\text{R.CHOH.CHNH}_2.\text{COOH} \rightarrow$ $\text{NH}_3 + \text{R.CH}_2.\text{CO.COOH}$
Desulphydration	$\text{R.CHSH.CHNH}_2.\text{COOH} + \text{H}_2\text{O}$ $\rightarrow \text{H}_2\text{S} + \text{NH}_3 + \text{R.CH}_2\text{CO COOH}$
Tryptophanase	Tryptophan $\rightarrow$ indole + pyruvate + NH_3
Cystathionase	Cystathionine $\rightarrow$ homoserine + pyruvate + NH_3
Decarboxylase	$\text{R.CHNH}_2 \text{ COOH} \rightarrow \text{R.CH}_2\text{NH}_2 + \text{CO}_2$
Amine oxidase	$\text{R.CH}_2\text{NH}_2 + \text{O} \rightarrow \text{R.CHO} + \text{NH}_3$
Synthetic changes e.g	Indole + serine $\rightarrow$ tryptophan + H_2O

Summing up we have:

Amino acid (A) + keto acid (B) $\leftrightarrows$ keto acid (A) + amino acid (B)

Vitamin B_6 deficiency in diets produces many consequences among which may be mentioned, for example, the development of anemia (probably due to the importance of the coenzyme in porphyrin synthesis) or such miscellaneous disturbances as the excretion of xanthurenic acid or diminished brain glutathione (507).

Possibly, however, the most important effects of interfering with vitamin B_6 catalyzed reactions are the cerebral consequences.

Convulsions are known to occur in vitamin B_6 deficiency in experimental animals and in some human infants (246) and it is known that, in these conditions, glutamic acid decarboxylase activity is decreased, due to the deficiency of the coenzyme (247). The occurrence of epileptiform seizures has been correlated with decreases of glutamic decarboxylase activities and levels of γ-aminobutyric acid (236), but it is not easy to prove that decrease of the latter amino acid is causally connected with the seizures as it does not penetrate into the brain with ease and hence administration may not be effective in diminishing the seizures. Convincing, but indirect, evidence of the involvement of γ-amino-butyric acid in convulsions comes from the facts that certain hydrazides (which react with pyridoxal) give rise to seizures and at the same time reduce glutamic decarboxylase activity and the level of γ-aminobutyric acid in rats (248). Among such convulsive hydrazides are thiosemicarbazide and isonicotinic acid hydrazide (isoniazid). The convulsions can be prevented by giving pyridoxamine. It should be pointed out, however, that high doses of pyridoxin produce symptoms not unlike those due to its deficiency. The mode of action of the carbazides differs from that of a convulsant such as Metrazol, where no changes in γ-aminobutyric acid or other amino acids in the brain take place after its administration (248). Pyridoxine is not a general anticonvulsant, but is specific for the convulsions of "pyridoxine-deficient" infants.

Vitamin B_6 deficiency will also produce a marked diminution of serotonin activity. It should be pointed out, however, that most of the serotonin in the body is found peripherally, in the mucosa of the stomach and intestine where it has an important role in gastric secretion and intestinal motility (for a review on serotonin, see 249). The significance of serotonin in brain function has still to be elucidated, but there can be little doubt that it is important. It is reported, for example, that small doses of 5-hydroxytrypophan influence the E.E.G. of patients in hepatic coma (250). Localization of serotonin in the brain stem areas suggests that it acts there, perhaps as a mediator of the central autonomic system (251).

Hydrazide administration to the animal seems not to diminish the levels of serotonin or the catecholamines.

Interference with amino acid decarboxylases *in vitro* may be brought about by amino acid analogues such as α-methylamino acids (e.g., α-methyltryptophane or α-methylhistidine). 2-Hydroxy-, and 2-5-dihydroxytryptophan are reported to be inhibitors of 5-hydroxytryptophan decarboxylase (252). *In vivo* inhibition of of dihydroxyphenylalanine decarboxylase can be brought about by administration of α-methyldihydroxyphenylalanine.

GLUTAMINE AND AMMONIA UTILIZATION

Glutamine is synthesized from glutamic acid and ammonia in the presence of brain (253), adenosine triphosphate and magnesium (or manganese) ions being needed for the reaction (254). The ATP may be supplied by the oxidative breakdown of glucose in the brain. In this manner brain slices *in vitro* remove ammonia (221). The following reaction takes place:

$$\text{Glutamate} + \text{ATP} + \text{NH}_3 = \text{Glutamine} + \text{ADP} + \text{P}i$$

Glutamine may undergo hydrolysis in brain, as well as in other parts of the body, by operation of glutaminase (253), which is inhibited by both isomers of glutamic acid as well as by α-methyl-glutamate (220).

The ammonia of the amide group of glutamine may be replaced by certain organic bases by the action of a glutamotransferase (256), as for example hydroxylamine:

$$\text{R.CO NH}_2 + \text{NH}_2\text{OH} \rightleftharpoons \text{R.CO.NHOH} + \text{NH}_3$$

It is possible that the wide distribution of glutamotransferase (and asparto-transferase) indicates the importance of glutamine (and asparagine) in peptide or protein synthesis.

Glutamine may also take part in transamination reactions (257), the existence of a glutamine-α keto acid transaminase in rat brain mitochondria having been described (258).

Glutamine formation provides one way, possibly quantitatively the most important way, in which free ammonium ions are removed in the brain cell (267). Brain cortex slices in presence of ammonium ions produce increased glutamine levels (223). This increase occurs at the expense of glutamate. There is an increase of 300-400% of glutamine, with some decrease of glutamate, in rat brain after injection of a lethal dose of ammonium chloride (259). Moreover, after hepatectomy in dogs a sixfold rise in cerebral glutamine occurs (260). Increased neuronal activity (as in convulsive conditions) is associated with increased ammonia formation (261). Vrba has suggested that the origin of ammonia found with increased neuronal and functional activity is associated with degradation and deamidation of protein components of the brain cell with liberation of ammonia (262). In fact, cerebral tissues can produce an amount of ammonia which is greater than the total amino-nitrogen of the tissue. It is evident that there are other sources of ammonia in the brain cell than the free amino acids and these are the subject of present day investigations. There is no doubt, however, that glutamine synthesis represents one way in which the content of ammonia in the brain is regulated. Recent studies (263) have shown that of all oxidizable substrates of the brain, glucose is the most effective in suppressing ammonia formation in brain slices, and this might be expected from the operation of the citric acid cycle in forming α-ketoglutarate which undergoes reductive amination to glutamate and then to glutamine (Fig. 1). Substances that counteract the suppressing action of glucose on ammonia formation in brain *in vitro* are isonicotinic acid hydrazide (which may work by immobilizing pyridoxal needed for the reaction) and cortisone (or hydrocortisone) whose mode of action is unknown.

MENTAL EFFECTS OF GLUTAMATE ADMINISTRATION

Beneficial effects of oral administration of glutamic acid to patients suffering from petit-mal epilepsy have been reported (264). Grand mal seizures are unaffected. Glutamic acid does not antagonize experimental electroshock convulsions in rats, but raises the threshold of pyridoxine deficient rats to electroshock (265).

There is a change in mental status when epileptics are given glutamine, an observation which led to administration of the amino acid to mentally retarded subjects. A favourable effect (266) was obtained, the reason for which is not at present clear (for a discussion see 267).

Glutamic acid administration to patients in insulin coma leads to consciousness being regained, a phenomenon which is considered due, or partly due, to the release of glucose by adrenaline (267) after administration of the amino acid.

Administration of glutamic acid analogues may give rise to symptoms resembling those due to interference with glutamate metabolism in the brain. Treatment of flour with nitrogen trichloride, a process formerly used in the "improvement" of flour, produces methionine sulphoximine (269) which is responsible for canine hysteria and neurological disorders in certain animals (monkeys, cats, ferrets but not rats, chickens or guinea pigs). The symptoms, as indicated by electroencephalography, resemble those of human epilepsy. Methionine sulphoximine inhibits glutamine synthesis in brain preparations and relieves the inhibition of acetylcholine synthesis induced by ammonium ions in the brain cell (270). Possibly the interference of methionine sulphoximine with glutamine metabolism is linked with its ability to produce neurological disorders.

PROTEIN TURNOVER IN BRAIN

There is evidence that glutamine has an important role in protein synthesis (271). The relatively large content of glutamine in the brain, and its important role in brain metabolism, raises the question of possible relationships between brain glutamine and brain proteins. At present there is little known on this subject, but there is increasing interest in the problems of protein synthesis and protein turnover in the brain cell.

Proteins constitute about 40% of the dry weight of the whole brain; some of them may have considerable metabolic activity. Stimulation of brain cortex slices by electrical impulses increases the incorporation of labelled phosphate into part of the phosphoprotein, the label being located on phosphoryl serine (272). This indicates, however, lability of phospate associated with proteins rather than of the proteins themselves.

The brain is rich in lipoproteins soluble in chloroform-methanol mixtures, and in nucleoproteins which are often associated with lipids. Some protein fractions (small in quantity) are associated with copper (273).

Gaitonde and Richter (274) administered labelled methionine (containing S^{35}) to rat brains via the cerebrospinal fluid, in order to by-pass the blood-brain barrier. Under these conditions there was a relatively rapid uptake of methionine into brain proteins. Even after administration by the intraperitoneal route the little amino acid that penetrated the brain was rapidly incorporated into protein. Calculations based on the uptake of S^{35} methionine $in\ vivo$ during a period of 20-60 minutes indicated a mean half-life of 14 days for the methionine bonds of the mixed proteins of the rat brain. Values of 6.2 to 15.2 days are reported for the half-life of mixed proteins of the mouse brain determined by use of C^{14}-lysine (275). Hyden (276) has found that vestibular stimulation affects protein content, enzyme activities and ribonucleic acid content in Deiter's nerve cells of the rabbit, an observation pointing to the mobility of nerve cell proteins and their response to changes in nerve function. Although there is no question of protein mobility as judged by the incorporation of radioactive amino acids into brain proteins, it should be borne in mind that the efficiency of brain (adult rat brain cortex slices) in using its available respiratory energy (as ATP) for the incorporation of glycine into its proteins is much less than that of rat liver slices, spleen, thymus or lung (277). Chick embryo is 80 times as effective as rat brain in this respect! The suggestion is made (277) that although the machinery for protein synthesis is present in the adult rat brain, it is not able to function as well as in other (especially potentially rapidly growing) tissues because the energy (ATP) is being used for the functional activities of the brain cell and there is less available for protein synthesis or for the amino acid activation that is preliminary to protein synthesis.

Amines, as well as amino acids, can be incorporated into brain proteins. Thus, labelled mescaline and β-phenylethylamine (278) and labelled ethanolamine, cadaverine and other amines (279) can be incorporated, possibly replacing the amide groups of the protein.

These facts indicate the rapid interchange of the organic constituents of the brain cell, steady-states of dynamic equilibria being set up that are changed during functional activity.

AMINE METABOLISM IN THE BRAIN

IT was shown about 25 years ago (280) that amines which it was thought might exist in the body in more than normal quantities in conditions of mental disorder, affect metabolism in the central nervous system. Tyramine, tryptamine and isoamylamine on being added to brain slices brought about a diminution in brain respiration. It was found that this diminution was due to the presence of an enzyme in the brain which brought about the oxidation of amines, including aliphatic amines, tyramine and tryptamine and this enzyme was termed amine oxidase (281). It proved to be identical with adrenaline oxidase (282). The course of oxidation of the amine was shown to be:

$$R.CH_2NH_2 + H_2O + O_2 \rightarrow R.CHO + NH_3 + H_2O_2$$

The diminution in oxygen consumption of brain cortex slices in the presence of the amine was found to be due to the formation of the corresponding aldehyde which had highly toxic effects on the brain respiratory system. However, the brain is equipped with enzymes that brings about the removal of aldehydes unless these are present in excessive quantities. Loeper (283) claimed that amines, including tyramine, tryptamine and histamine may circulate in the blood under certain pathological conditions (e.g., liver disease and shock). Nieuwenhuyzen (284) demonstrated that intravenous injection of tryptamine and other amines may give rise to a condition resembling catatonia. Further work carried out with brain cortex slices showed that amine analogues, e.g., amphetamine, inhibit amine oxidase (285) preventing aldehyde formation. It was pointed out that the relative stimulatory effects of amphetamine and its derivatives on the central nervous system bore a parallelism to their effects on amine oxidase. Relatively little interest was taken in this work at the time, (though it was known that phenylethylamine derivatives were potent in their neurological effects (286) a number of them giving rise to catatonic-like states) chiefly because there was no evidence that the amines in question were actually present in brain. The recent discoveries of amines such as tryptamine, serotonin and noradrenaline in the brain have focused interest anew in the significance of amine oxidase in brain metabolism and function. A symposium devoted to this subject has been held recently (306). The biologically active amines that are receiving much attention today are dopamine (dihydroxyphenylethylamine), tyramine. o-tyramine, serotonin, tryptamine, histamine, γ-aminobutyric acid, carnitine (β-oxy-butyrobetaine) and choline and acetyl-choline. These substances can all be formed from dietary amino acids and are to be found in animal tissues where they may be highly localized.

SEROTONIN

After the detection and isolation of serotonin by Rapport *et al.* (287), it became evident that it is widely distributed in many varieties of living cells. A recent review of its biochemistry and function in the nervous system has been made by Udenfriend *et al.* (288). It is present in the gastrointestinal tract, in blood platelets and in brain. Its distribution in various parts of the brain together with the relative activities of the enzymes responsible for its formation and destruction (i.e., 5-hydroxytryptophan decarboxylase and amine oxidase) are shown in Table 20, the data being obtained by Udenfriend *et al.* (288). The hypothalamus, midbrain and caudate nucleus (but not the cerebral cortex) are relatively rich in serotonin and the same general distribution is found for 5-hydroxytryptophan decarboxylase which is present in the soluble cytoplasm of the cell. Amine oxidase is more evenly

TABLE 20

RELATIVE ACTIVITIES OF AMINE OXIDASE AND 5-HYDROXYTRYPTOPHAN DECARBOXYLASE AND SEROTONIN CONTENT OF BRAIN TISSUES (288)

Tissue (Dog)	Amine oxidase γ serotonin destroyed	5 HTP Decarboxylase γ serotonin formed	Serotonin γ/g
Caudate nucleus	702	306	1.0
Hypothalamus	1660	117	1.6
Mid Brain	1254	98	1.0
Thalamus	940	38	0.5
Cerebellum	930	9	0.07
Cortex (Cerebral)	843	7	0.2

distributed through the brain and is usually associated with tissue mitochondria.

A potent inhibitor of amine oxidase is iproniazid (1-isonicotinyl-2-isopropylhydrazine) (289) which, in contrast to amphetamine, is highly active *in vivo*. The inhibitor affects serotonin and tyramine oxidations similarly, the oxidation product of serotonin being 5-hydroxyindoleacetic acid which is normally found in urine. Most inhibitors of amine oxidase are relatively inactive *in vivo*, iproniazid being an exception. Administration of this inhibitor leads to a marked increase of endogenous serotonin, this being increased still more by giving a dose of 5-hydroxytryptophan or tryptophan. The relative inactivities of amine oxidase inhibitors *in vivo* is probably connected with difficulty of penetration to the sites of the enzyme in the living animal.

Administered serotonin is rapidly oxidized in the body, but much of it is taken up by the blood platelets, which are also able to bind other amines such as adrenaline and histamine. Apparently blood platelets are able to accumulate these bases against a concentration gradient, active transport taking place. Such concentration of serotonin is not unique to blood platelets for it is present in a bound form in brain. Such "binding" was demonstrated many years ago with acetylcholine and will be referred to later.

Increase in brain serotonin by iproniazid parallels the potentiation of central effects. Where there is overproduction of serotonin, as in metastatic malignant carcinoids, the syndrome consists of cardio-vascular disturbance, flushing, diarrhoea, and asthmatic attacks but there is no mental disturbance. Circulating serotonin evidently does not penetrate into the brain. The psychomimetic drug, lysergic acid diethylamide (LSD), which like serotonin contains the indole nucleus, is said to owe its effects on the nervous system by interfering with the physiological effects of serotonin in the brain (290). Shore *et al.* (291) have given evidence that brain serotonin is released from the bound form to the free form by the rauwolfia alkaloids. These also release noradrenaline from brain. After administration of reserpine (to rabbits) the brain levels of these amines decline as they are released and destroyed by amine oxidase (292). Possibly they act by preventing concentrative uptake of the amines, so that the high cellular concentration of

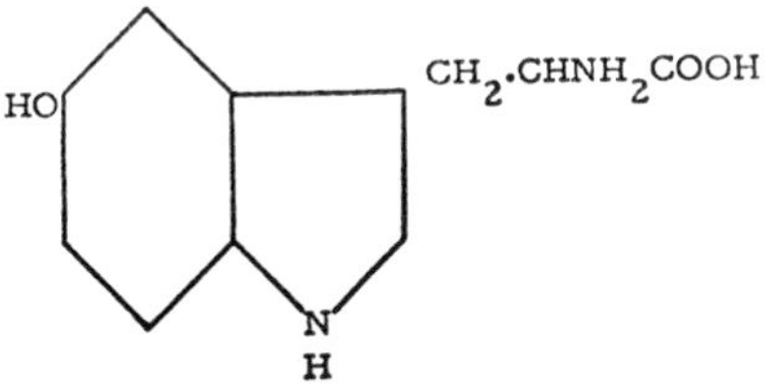

5 - Hydroxytryptophan

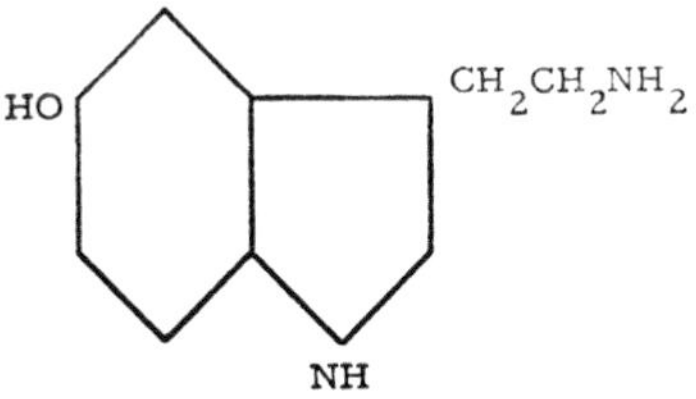

Serotonin

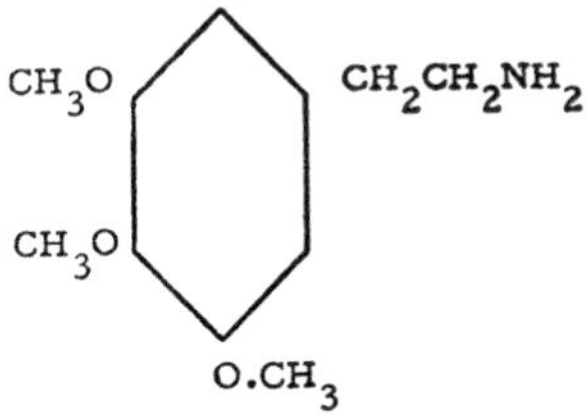

Mescaline

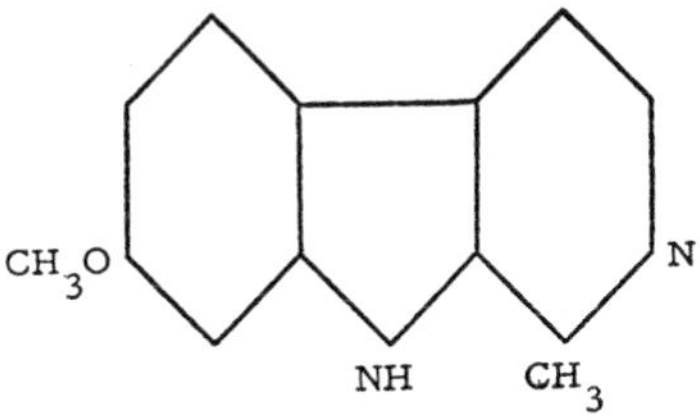

Harmine

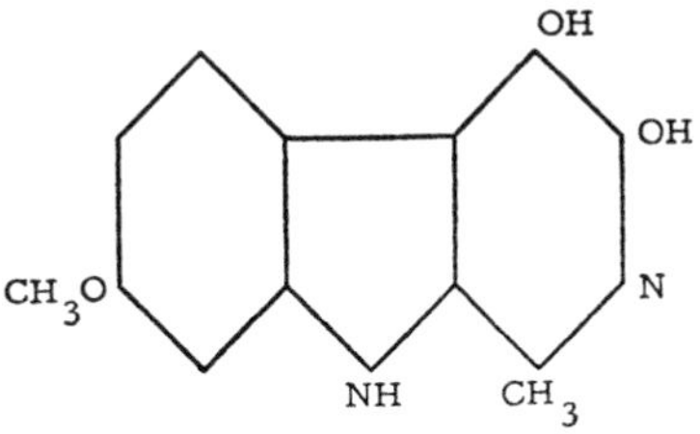

Harmaline

the amines diffuse out without the opposing active transport into the cells taking place. Iproniazid is not able appreciably to restore serotonin or noradrenaline levels after they have been depleted by reserpine (511) but isopropylhydrazine is more effective in increasing brain serotonin levels (512) after depletion.

The central effects of reserpine persist long after the drug has disappeared from the brain which is in accordance with the foregoing explanation of its action. After the amine oxidase has been inhibited by iproniazid, the depleting effect of reserpine is reduced and its tranquilizing effect is changed into an excitatory one, due to the accumulation of free amines. Excess serotonin (as found after administration of large doses of 5-hydroxytryptophan) has the opposite effect to reserpine (511).

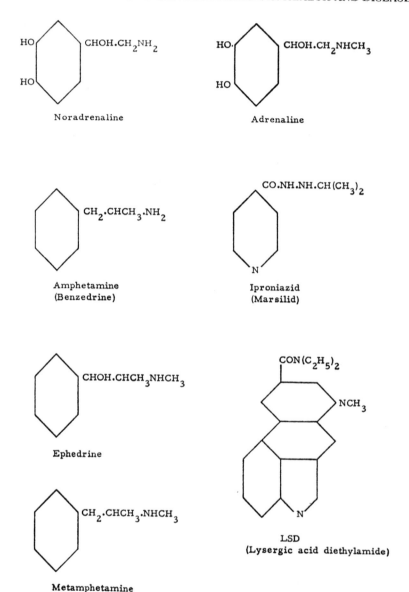

Noradrenaline

Adrenaline

Amphetamine
(Benzedrine)

Iproniazid
(Marsilid)

Ephedrine

Metamphetamine

LSD
(Lysergic acid diethylamide)

The presence of serotonin in invertebrate animals, and its pharmacological behaviour there, led Welsh (305) to suggest that serotonin may be a normal mediator for the excitatory nerves of such organisms.

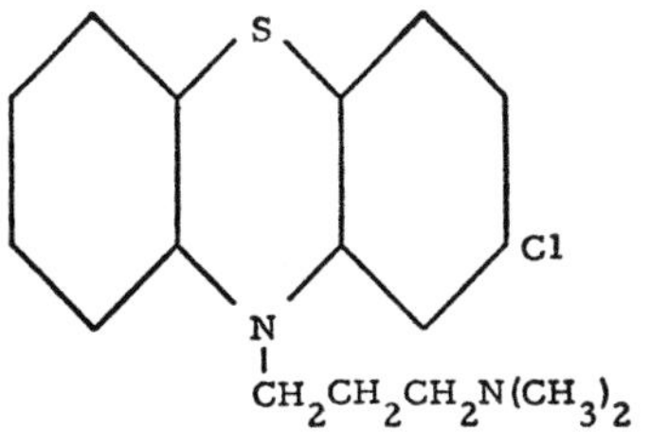

S

Cl

N

$CH_2CH_2CH_2N(CH_3)_2$

Chlorpromazine

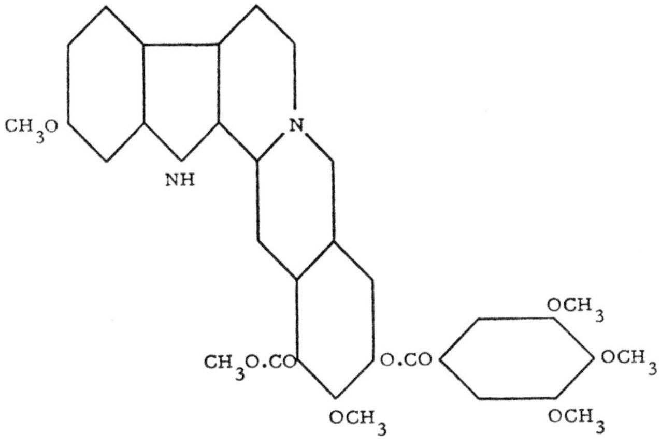

CH_3O

N

NH

$CH_3O.CO$

$O.CO$

OCH_3

OCH_3

OCH_3

OCH_3

OCH_3

Reserpine

The harmala alkaloids (harmaline and harmine) prove to be potent reversible amine oxidase inhibitors. They are active at $10^{-7}M$ and ten times more active *in vitro* than the potent hydrazine inhibitors (252). They are known to have central actions.

The biological importance of indole containing compounds in influencing cell metabolism is becoming very evident. Indole itself has a powerful narcotic-like effect on brain metabolism *in vitro* (280). Indole derivatives undergo oxidation in the liver to hydroxylated products and possibly this is the main mechanism of their detoxication.

CATECHOLAMINES

Peripheral adrenergic neurons are characterized by their ultimate release of noradrenaline. Part of the cerebral noradrenaline is not situated in the adrenergic vasomotor fibres. It is not found in myelinated fibres but in specific regions of grey matter consisting of nerve cells, glia and non-myelinated fibres (293). The richest regions are in the lower part of the brain, the hypothalamus and area postrema. The concentration in cat brain hypothalamus is about $1.4\gamma/g$. fresh tissue. In ox nerves the highest concentrations $(8.5\text{-}18.5\gamma/g.)$ are in the splenic nerves, which consist almost exclusively of adrenergic axons, whilst ox brain gives figures of $0.02\text{-}0.2\gamma/g.$ (294)

Some representative values, as given by von Euler, are shown in Table 21.

So far as the peripheral functions of adrenaline and noradrenaline are concerned, von Euler (294) remarks, "it appears that noradrenaline should be looked upon as an 'everyday maintenance' hormone engaged in normal vegetative life processes whereas adrenaline, as pointed out by Cannon, occupies the role as an emergency stimulant with more differentiated actions. It is obvious that during an emergency situation it is not necessary that a rise of

TABLE 21

DISTRIBUTION OF ADRENALINE AND NORADRENALINE (294)

Species	Nerve	Adrenaline $\gamma/g.$	Noradrenaline $\gamma/g.$
Man	Lumbar sympathetic	0.33–1.2	3.2
Sheep	Brain	0.005	0.08
Rabbit	Brain	0.02	0.2
Cattle	Brain	0.007	0.07

blood pressure should occur and thus adrenaline serves well; on the other hand there is no need for increased oxygen consumption and mobilization of sugar when vasomotor reflexes are operating for the purpose of maintaining homeostasis of blood pressure. Here noradrenaline is more appropriate. Thus the functions of the two hormones seem to be separate and distinct; however, it is quite possible that the two hormones may at times act in concert."

Reserpine has a large effect on hypothalamic noradrenaline causing losses amounting to 60% with small doses and to 97% with large doses (293). Drugs such as caffeine, leptazol, ephedrine and chlorpromazine do not affect the brain content of noradrenalin, but picrotoxin, ether, nicotine and morphine bring about falls and exhibit a common action in stimulating the sympathetic centres. The effect of reserpine differs from that of the latter drugs (293), for it causes a loss of noradrenaline from both brain and the peripheral sympathetic system. "Prolonged treatment by reserpine" according to Vogt (293) "produces the most complete form of (functional) sympathectomy, since the drug has access to sites which are not amenable to surgical removal."

In contrast to serotonin, whose concentration remains high when iproniazid precedes the administration of reserpine, loss of noradrenaline from hypothalamic and sympathetic ganglia is not prevented by iproniazid (293), presumably because another route of inactivation (? methylation) occurs.

At present, much interest is being taken in the enzymes concerned with the formation and destruction of products derived from adrenaline and tryptamine because of their psychopharmacological effects. Weil-Malherbe (255) has suggested that there is a definite connection between the level of mental activity and the concentration of adrenaline in the plasma.

Noradrenaline is formed from dihydroxyphenylalanine by enzymatic oxidation, the enzyme involved, dopamine oxidase, being located in the brain (e.g., hypothalamus, caudate nucleus) and in the adrenal medulla. It is apparently absent from the brain cortex and there is little in the cerebellum. The presence of both ascorbic acid and ATP is needed for the oxidation. Both adrenaline and noradrenaline in the brain are synthesized locally (308).

"Physical" binding of amines, or concentrative uptake into cells or structures, wherein the amines are not broken down, is a form of pharmacological inactivation. Chemical inactivation occurs through oxidation by amine oxidase or methylation by o-methyltransferase which is widely distributed throughout the nervous system (514). It is found in largest quantity in the liver and pancreas.

Axelrod and his colleagues have shown (307) that the o-methylation of adrenaline to methyladrenaline (metanephrine) by catechol-o-methyl-transferase, a system that requires S-adenosylmethionine and magnesium ions, precedes the deamination by amine oxidase The presence of iproniazid increases the output *in vivo* of labelled metanephrine from administered labelled adrenaline with little effect on the output of adrenaline itself. It increases markedly, however, the output of labelled metanephrine when the latter is administered *in vivo*. Metanephrine may be excreted as a glucuronide or as the oxidized product viz. 3-methoxy-4-hydroxy mandelic acid. The enzyme accomplishing the methylation affects L-adrenaline, dihydroxyphenylethylamine, and catechol but not tyramine or tyrosine; it is called catechol-o-methyl-transferase. It is present in most tissues (liver, glandular tissues) and in all parts of the brain in amounts adequate to cope with the catecholamines present. Pyrogallol and catechol inhibit the methylation of noradrenaline *in vitro* and *in vivo* (307). Brain levels of catecholamines are increased after administration of an amine oxidase inhibitor (Brodie *et al.* 316).

The wide pharmacological implications of inhibitors of amine metabolism (inhibitors of amine oxidase, amino acid hydrolases and decarboxylases, amine-methyltransferases) cannot be discussed here. The subject is growing at a fast rate (see 306) and promises to have much bearing on the understanding and treatment of cerebral dysfunction and mental disorders with which amine metabolism is associated.

It is not yet understood why the various amines that have been mentioned are physiologically active. A point of view that may be worth exploring is that these amines exert, at the specific sites in the brain cell where they are located, cationic effects, modifying the ionic balance that controls, directly or indirectly, energy and transport relations. Further reference to this suggestion will be made later.

HISTAMINE

Mammalian nervous tissue contains histamine but its concentration in various locations varies widely. Thus its amounts in man are (309): brain $0.1\gamma/g.$; spinal cord $0.1\gamma/g.$; spinal roots $0.3\gamma/g.$; preganglionic sympathetic $4\gamma/g.$; vagus $3\gamma/g.$; postganglionic sympathetic $6\gamma/g.$ The corresponding amounts in dog are two to three times these values. It is derived from histidine by histidine decarboxylase which is present in certain nervous tissues (especially postganglionic autonomic fibres). It is present in mast cells, though not invariably so (310). Histamine, like serotonin, is stored in mast cells, and may be released by reserpine. Histamine is oxidized by histaminase or diamine oxidase, not by amine oxidase; however N-methyl-histamine is oxidized by the latter enzyme (395). The function of histamine in the brain is unknown; possibly it is concerned with vasodilatation and change of permeability of blood capillaries in the nervous system (310). Antihistamines have central effects, but these drugs are known to have effects on other systems besides those involving histamine and their central effects do not parallel their antihistamine activities.

ACETYLCHOLINE

Important in the growth of concepts of the relation between brain biochemistry and brain function has been the discovery of brain mechanisms concerned with the synthesis and breakdown of acetylcholine. Much has been written about the physiological significance of acetylcholine and there are outstanding reviews on the subject (e.g., 311,312,313,314) to which the reader is referred. It is evident from data accumulated since the early studies of Dale (315) and his colleagues (316) that acetylcholine, liberated at nerve endings, acts as a transmitter at the neuro-muscular junction and this provides a reasonable explanation for the effects of curare, which blocks the action of the transmitter, and of eserine which prolongs its action. The discovery of the action of acetylcholine on the end plate potential (317) further strengthened this conclusion. There is also good evidence for the conclusion that acetylcholine is the synaptic transmitter in auto-nomic ganglia (311) and that it mediates parasympathetic trans-mission. That acetylcholine is involved in conduction of the nerve impulse along the axon as well as junctional transmission has been suggested by a number of workers and particularly by Nachmansohn who has recently summarized his evidence and conclusions (318).

So far as the role of acetylcholine in the central nervous system is concerned, evidently it acts as a central synaptic transmitter but it is not the only one (314). This view is mainly based on results obtained on the distribution of the enzyme systems responsible for acetylcholine synthesis, on changes in acetylcholine content of the brain under a variety of conditions, on release of acetylcholine from the central nervous system, and on the central effects of acetylcholine, anticholinesterases and of atropine.

ACETYLCHOLINE SYNTHESIS IN THE BRAIN

Acetylcholine undergoes rapid hydrolysis by cholinesterase whose activities in various parts of the brain are of obvious importance to brain function. The pharmacological effects of cholinesterase inhibitors, of which there are a great variety, point to the significance of the enzyme in neurophysiological and neurochemical phenomena. This is seen not only in the effects of quaternary ammonium bases, of prostigmine and its analogues, of curare etc. in man and in higher animals, but in the effects of anticholinesterases such as fluorphosphonates and polyphosphates that have obtained economic importance as insecticides.

The existence of a cholinesterase inhibitor, eserine, made it possible to demonstrate for the first time in 1936 the synthesis of acetycholine by brain cortex slices under physiological conditions (319). It was shown that the synthesis by brain slices could only be accomplished aerobically in presence of glucose, mannose, pyruvate or lactate. Glutamate and α-glycerophosphate were effective to a small extent but fructose, galactose, succinate and acetate were ineffective. It was suggested that the energy derived from carbohydrate breakdown was responsible for acetylcholine synthesis, and the results indicated a link between the products of glucose metabolism and the synthesis of acetylcholine. Moreover brain was almost unique in this property for neither kidney, spleen, liver nor testis showed the synthesis and muscle showed it only feebly. Stedman and Stedman (320) later demonstrated acetylcholine formation in brain, but their results showed little evidence of biosynthesis but rather the fact that a bound, pharmacologically inert, form of acetylcholine could under their experimental conditions (maceration with chloroform) liberate free acetylcholine. Mann et al. (321) discovered a bound form of acetylcholine, not pharmacologically active, in brain, that under a variety of conditions forms free acetycholine. Such conditions are, for example, the presence of denaturing agents, excess chloroform or acid or high concentration of potassium ions. The bound form is produced by brain slices under physiological conditions but not anaerobically or in the absence of a suitable substrate such as glucose. Free acetylcholine is released by venom lecithinase and it was suggested (322) that bound acetylcholine is simply acetylcholine held within the brain mitochondria, which when attacked by lecithinase, liberates acetylcholine. Other subcellular particles might act similarly (323).

There is, in fact, evidence to suggest that "synaptic vesicles" which are small subcellular particles found in the presynaptic axoplasm in a wide variety of synapses, may be the sites in which acetylcholine is stored pending discharge into the intermembranal space of the synapse. These vesicles may represent quantal units of the transmitter substance (468, 503).

The conclusion that glucose or a breakdown product of glucose is important for the biosynthesis of acetycholine in brain was confirmed by experiments of MacIntosh (324) on perfusion of the superior cervical ganglion of the cat. Fructose was not able to enhance acetylcholine formation in perfused ganglia.

The discovery of acetylcholine synthesis by enzymatic means (319) had considerable consequences for it was the first demonstration *in vitro* of an enzyme controlled acetylation. Nachmansohn and Machado later advanced the subject when they showed (325) that the synthesis of acetylcholine will occur anaerobically with a brain extract so long as ATP is present. It thus became obvious that ATP derived from carbohydrate metabolism in brain can be used for a brain acetylation. Further work made it clear that the synthesis was dependent on a heat stable cofactor studied by Nachmansohn, by Feldberg and by Lipmann who with his colleagues showed its importance, as coenzyme A, in acetylations and biosynthetic processes. Increased K^+ in the medium surrounding brain cortex slices increases the rate of acetylcholine synthesis (89), a phenomenon which occurs also with application of electric impulses (327). When Na^+ is wholly replaced by K^+, however, acetylcholine synthesis ceases (89). The following scheme represents the cycle of events involving the synthesis and breakdown of acetylcholine in the brain:

$$
\begin{array}{ccc}
\text{Pyruvate} + \text{DPN} + \text{CoA} & & \text{choline} \\
\text{or} & \rightarrow \text{Acetyl-CoA} & \rightarrow \qquad \text{Tissue acetylcholine} + \text{CoA} \\
\text{ATP} + \text{CoA} + \text{Acetate} & & \text{choline} \\
& & \text{acetylase} \qquad \text{(Bound} + \text{Free)}
\end{array}
$$

Increase K^+/Ca^{++}
or
Electric impulses

Acetate + Choline $\longleftarrow$ Free Acetylcholine
choline
esterase

Feldberg and Vogt (328) have studied the synthesis of acetylcholine in various regions of the central nervous system of dogs. Dog retina is rich in choline acetylase (which catalyses the reaction between choline and acetyl-CoA) but the optic nerve is free of the enzyme. Results given in Table 22, collected by McIlwain from the values of Hebb and Silver (329) and Burgen and Chipman (330) show the preponderance of choline acetylase and of choline esterase in the caudate nucleus.

TABLE 22
ACETYCHOLINE SYNTHESIS AND HYDROLYSIS IN DOG BRAIN

Part of brain	Acetylcholine synthesis μmoles/g./hr. formed	Acetylcholine esterase μmoles/g./hr. decomposed	Acetylcholine hydrolyzed by pseudocholine esterase μmoles/g./hr. decomposed
Cerebral Cortex	1.3–3.7	60–100	2–4
Cerebellar cortex	0.09	460	0.5
Caudate nucleus	13	1900	2
Thalamus	3.1	220–310	5
Hypothalamus	2	190	11

ACETYLCHOLINE CONTENT OF THE BRAIN

The acetylcholine content of brain varies according to functional activity of the brain. Thus a normal value of 1.25γ/g. in rat brain fell to 0.87γ/g. in states of excitement and 0.56γ/g. in convulsions. It was raised to 1.76γ/g. in deep anaesthesia. There are various ways of interpreting such values as these. One way, which may be borne in mind, is that release of acetylcholine from the bound form, by stimulation as already mentioned, results in attack of the free ester by cholinesterase, so that the total acetylcholine will necessarily fall. This explanation is similar to that given for the effects of reserpine on brain serotonin.

Experiments of MacIntosh and Oborin (334) led to the conclusion that there is a close correlation between acetylcholine content of the brain, electrical cortical activity and release of acetylcholine from the cortex (314).

The rate of acetylcholine formation *in vitro* in the brains of polyneuritic pigeons is smaller than that in the normal. The addition of small amounts of thiamine restores the rate of synthesis, confirming the conclusion that pyruvate metabolism *in vivo* is intimately associated with acetylcholine synthesis (332).

Results concerning the effects of substances on acetylcholine synthesis using brain preparations (extracts, powders) whilst of value in throwing light on the mechanism of synthesis must be applied to the brain *in vivo* with great caution. The reason is that use of brain extracts, etc. involves artificial conditions whose effects have to be assessed carefully for interpretations to be made which can be applied to intact brain. For example, it is easy to demonstrate that glucose inhibits the synthesis of acetylcholine in brain powders at concentrations similar to those in blood. The reason is that the glucose immobilizes part of the ATP necessary for synthesis by conversion to hexose phosphate. The inhibition *in vitro* by glucose can be abolished by simply adding nicotinamide to the extract, for this inhibits the breakdown of DPN by DPNase (161), allows glycolysis to take place and ATP necessary for acetylcholine synthesis is not immobilized (333). It is evident that the synthesis of acetycholine in brain depends on the integrity of the DPN system to ensure optimal respiratory activity (333).

The existence of esters of choline, other than acetylcholine, in mammalian and invertebrate tissues has now been demonstrated e.g. propionylcholine (484), butyrylcholine (485), imidazole-acetylcholine (486) in mammalian tissues, and other choline esters (e.g. the urocanic ester) in invertebrate tissue (487). Berry and Whittaker (488), studying the acyl-group specificity of sheep-pigeon-, and rat brain choline acetylase (see also 489), by coupling the enzyme with a preparation from pigeon liver capable of activating various fatty acids, have shown that the enzyme is able to synthesize all the *n*-acyl cholines up to C_6 and also palmitoyl choline. Pigeon brain choline acetylase has a high degree of specificity, as it is able to synthesize only acetyl- and propionyl-choline. The physiological significance of the synthesis of the homologues of acetylcholine by brain tissue is not clear. It is doubtful whether such homologues actually occur in brain tissue (488); if they are synthesized *in vivo* they must be broken down very rapidly to account for their lack of accumulation even in small quantities.

CHOLINESTERASES AND ANTI-CHOLINESTERASES

Activities of the cholinesterases (true acetylcholinesterase specific for acetylcholine and pseudocholinesterase which can attack a variety of esters) vary according to their location in the brain (Table 22). A very great amount of work has been carried out by ingenious and useful techniques (e.g., that of Koelle, 326) to locate the enzyme in the nerve cell. Acetylcholinesterase occurs not only at nerve endings but along the whole nerve fibre.

The central action of acetylcholine and the anticholinesterases are very similar, the effects of the latter drugs lasting longer. The electric discharges (as seen in the E.E.G.) produced by these drugs resemble grand mal discharges. Applied to the hypothalamus, 8γ to 59γ eserine can produce sympathetic effects similar to some obtained at that site by electric stimulation. Prostigmine is valuable in practice for its peripheral action in myasthenia gravis. The use of DFP (diosopropylfluorophosphate) is limited because of its central actions which include E.E.G. changes (antagonized by atropine) emotional lability and insomnia. The studies of Wilson and others have shown that phosphorylation of the enzyme is brought about by DFP and polyphosphates and that such an enzyme may react with hydroxylamine to yield reactivated enzyme and hydroxylamine phosphate. Reactivation may also be accomplished by compounds containing amino, pyridyl, guanidine, hydroxyl or mercapto groups (335).

Atropine is not an antagonist of all the central actions of acetylcholine and the anticholinesterases but it inhibits many of them. In man, severe atropine poisoning produces a psychotic state with hallucinations. It may be that psychotic like states are partly due to inhibition of cholinergic transmissions in subcortical structures. Catatonic states can be produced in animals by applications of excessive quantities of acetylcholine (314).

ACETYLCHOLINE MEMBRANE REACTIONS

There is evidence to indicate that acetylcholine affects permeability relations at cell membranes (336). At cholinergic synapses, including the neuromuscular junction, it causes depolarization of the post-synaptic membrane by an increase of membrane permeability to Na^+ and K^+. The permeability increase is not to Na^+ alone as it seems to be in axon conduction (503). The mechanism by which acetylcholine causes depolarization, or permeability changes, is not known.

Acetylcholine (in presence of eserine) at small concentrations, or carbamylcholine, brings about an increase in the labelling of lipid phosphorus in brain slices (from guinea pig or pigeon) exposed under normal respiratory conditions to P^{32} (337). This interesting phenomenon, not yet clearly explained, may throw light on the mode of action of acetylcholine at brain cell membranes.

AMMONIA TOXICITY AND HEPATIC COMA ("HEPATO-CEREBRAL INTOXICATION")

Ammonium ions play a definite role in brain metabolism and presumably, therefore, in brain function. Normally found even in hibernating animals (338), they increase in amount with increased brain activity after awakening of the animals. Brain ammonia increases in convulsive states, or after direct stimulation of the brain, but the origin of brain ammonia, as already pointed out, is not well understood. The problem remains as to why ammonium ions should produce neurotoxic effects. Ammonium ions increase aerobic glycolysis of the brain cell (219) but this is unlikely to be the reason for ammonia toxicity in the nervous system. Ammonium ions inhibit aerobic synthesis of acetylcholine in brain slices *in vitro* (270) probably by increasing the rate of synthesis of glutamine from α ketoglutarate and glutamate (Fig. 1) and thereby diminishing the available ATP needed for acetylcholine formation and other functional activities of the brain. This seems a possible mechanism but another that may be borne in mind is competitive action of ammonium ions with the organic amines that play so important a role in regulating brain function.

Clinically, hepatic pre-coma is a condition of mental confusion, and drowsiness, leading to stupor and coma (339). It is possible to induce hepatic coma by feeding ammonium salts or proteins to patients with severe cirrhosis. Ammonium ion concentrations in arterial and venous blood are increased in hepatic coma but not in liver disease without neurological manifestations. The most effective treatment includes complete withdrawal of protein from the diet with antibiotic treatment to affect bacteria in the gastrointestinal tract with later gradual increase of proteins to the point of toleration. The data offer support for the hypothesis that ammonia is an important agent in the development of hepatic coma (339).

Intravenous arginine and glutamic acid are now used commonly in treatment of hepatic coma, sometimes with remarkable, though usually temporary, alleviation of symptoms. The former amino acid is supposed to act by stimulating urea synthesis (and thereby removal of ammonia), the latter by taking up ammonia to form glutamine.

The fact that 5-hydroxytryptophan given intravenously has in some cases caused a temporary improvement in the E.E.G. of patients with hepatic coma, has led to the suggestion that, in hepatic coma, there may be a reduction of circulating essential substrates of brain metabolism as well as an increase of toxic substances (469).

CEREBRAL DYSFUNTION DUE TO SYSTEMIC DISEASES

As Conn has pointed out (470) the neurological abnormalities found in severe liver disease have much in common with those observed in such diverse conditions as pulmonary insufficiency, hypomagnesemia, bromism, hypokalemia, gastro-intestinal malabsorptive syndromes, uremia and others. In each of these, for example, "liver flap" (asterixis) may be observed. The E.E.G. pattern in all these diseases is very similar — consisting chiefly of bilaterally synchronous slow delta waves and theta waves of increased voltage. In those cases where it is due to pulmonary insufficiency and congestive heart failure, the administration of oxygen reverses these changes. It seems unlikely that any specific metabolic derangement, such as hyperammonemia or hypoglycemia, electrolyte deficiencies or pH changes, can account for the neurological abnormalities in these diseases. Rather it seems that this variety of disorders may all disturb some common neurochemical pathway by different mechanisms.

The factors responsible for cerebral dysfunction in uremia are probably multiple. If serum electrolytes, especially potassium, can be kept at about normal levels, in cases of acute renal failure, mental changes are slower to develop. External haemodialysis can effect reversal of these, but the extent of the reversal is variable. It seems to be independent of the removal of urea (340).

WILSON'S DISEASE

Wilson's disease, hepato-lenticular degeneration, is a simple recessive hereditary disorder, in which there occurs a group of metabolic changes involving, liver, kidney and the central nervous system (295). It develops usually in adolescence or early adult life and is characterized by liver cirrhosis associated wth degeneration in the putamen, globus pallidus and caudate nuclei. Progressive intellectual deterioration and mental defect occur, as well as a mild ataxia.

There is, in this disorder, a greatly increased urinary excretion of amino acids, about two and a half times their normal level, but the level of plasma amino acids is not sufficiently raised to account for the high rate of excretion. Some amino acids are more affected than others, the abnormalities being larger than those seen in severe liver disorders such as occur in alcoholic cirrhosis. Cumings (296) demonstrated that abnormalities in the copper content of the liver and brain (especially the basal ganglia) occur in this disorder, the amounts being unusually high (about seven or eight fold their normal content). The serum content of copper is low, about one half normal; that in the urine is very high. It may be noted that three copper containing proteins have been found in brain, a cerebrocuprein having been isolated from human brain containing 0.3% copper (510).

It is now thought that the basis of the disease is a deficiency of ceruloplasmin, which is a copper-α-2-globulin normally present is blood. This deficiency permits deposition of copper in various tissues, causing cirrhosis in the liver, gliosis in the brain, amino acid excretion from the kidneys and is manifested in the eyes as the Kayser-Fleischer rings (466). The disease is thus analogous to haemophilia, agammaglobulinaemia, sickle cell anaemia and other diseases characterized by a defect in the synthesis of a particular protein

The disease process may be at least partly halted by administration of copper chelating agents such as BAL or EDTA (Versene). Penicillamine (dimethylcysteine) is said to be the most effective such agent (466) but Cumings (519) does not consider that it is as effective clinically as BAL. It is possible, however, that part of the disease process, the cirrhosis for example, is not dependent on the defect in copper metabolism, and therefore may not be susceptible to treatment with copper chelating agents.

AMINO ACID METABOLISM AND CEREBRAL DYSFUNCTION

PHENYLKETONURIA

ANOTHER congenital biochemical abnormality associated with mental defect is phenylketonuria, associated with disturbed phenylalanine metabolism, in which phenylpyruvic acid is excreted in the urine. It is inherited as a simple recessive. Originally discovered by Folling (298), the disease was called phenylpyruvic oligophrenia, but it seemed that a more appropriate name, in view of related inherited biochemical abnormalities, would be phenylketonuria (302) and this term is now used widely.

The biochemical disturbance responsible for the disorder is a deficiency of the liver enzyme, phenylalanine hydroxylase, which normally converts phenylalanine to tyrosine (299). As phenylalanine is a normal ingredient of most protein foodstuffs, the phenylalanine metabolism is diverted towards the production of phenylpyruvic acid and related substances which accumulate in the blood and are excreted in the urine.

It is estimated that about 1% of the population of U.S. mental institutions are phenylketonurics. Most of these are fair haired with blue eyes. The majority of phenylketonuric patients have a very low grade intelligence, except possibly in the first few months of life. Epileptic seizures occur in some of the patients and encephalographic abnormalities are found in about 80% (300).

A rational therapy, consisting of the administration of a phenylalanine-free diet, has been devised and has given encouraging results (301). Clinical signs improve; there is a decrease in epileptic seizures and disappearance of E.E.G. abnormalities. Neurological behaviour improves, but improvement of mental deficiency seems not to occur except in young patients. Thus early diagnosis is essential for any hope of successful treatment.

There is no doubt that the mental defect is associated with the production in the body of products of metabolism of phenylalanine, not normally found when the course of oxidation through tyrosine proceeds. Phenylpyruvate is excreted in non-phenylketonurics only after ingestion of D-phenylalanine or phenylpyruvate itself (302), but thiamine deficient rats excrete small quantities of the keto acid. The amount of phenylalanine in the plasma of phenylketonuric patients varies between 15 and 60 mg. per 100 ml. (about 30 times the normal concentration). Besides phenylpyruvic acid, there are also excreted relatively large quantities of p-hydroxyphenyllactic and p-hydroxyphenylacetic acids (303). Phenylpyruvic acid itself is not metabolized by phenylketonurics as rapidly as by normal subjects (302) but this may be partly due to the absence of phenylalanine hydroxylase, as presumably some phenylpyruvic acid will produce phenylalanine by transamination.

Some light may be thrown on the connection of mental disturbance with phenylketonuria by the observation (304,474) that both L-phenylalanine and phenylpyruvic acid interfere with tyrosine metabolism and may therefore interfere with the production of catecholamines or other hormones from tyrosine.

"MAPLE SYRUP URINE" DISEASE

This is a very rare familial disease which has been described in recent years. It is characterized by the urinary excretion of abnormally large quantities of valine, leucine and isoleucine together with the corresponding keto acids and hydroxy acids. There is also excessive excretion of indoleacetic and indolelactic acids. It is presumed that the disease is due to an enzyme deficiency

Mackenzie and Woolf (467) have suggested the name "carboxylase deficiency disease" for the disorder. The prognosis in this condition is probably worse than in phenylketonuria; most cases have died young.

HARTNUP DISEASE

Hartnup disease is a rare disease, inherited as simple recessive, which is characterized by a disorder in the intermediary metabolism of tryptophan. Generally first diagnosed as pellagra, because of the presence of cutaneous photosensitivity and rash, similar to that in pellagra, there is also a neurological disorder which is distinct from that of pellagra. There are signs, for example, of cerebellar ataxia. Mental deficiency occurs late and is slowly progressive. There is a characteristic aminoaciduria (though plasma amino acid levels are normal) and high excretion rates of indican, indole-3-acetic acid, and indole-3-acetyl glutamine (448).

A rather similar neurologic disorder, but associated with high blood serotonin levels, with intermittent face flushing similar to that seen in the syndrome of malignant carcinoid, has recently been observed in an adult. The symptomatology was aggravated by reserpine, in the case described, suggesting that, despite an excess production of serotonin, there was a functional deficiency of serotonin in the brain (449).

LIPID METABOLISM IN THE BRAIN

ABOUT half the dry matter of brain consists of lipids which play a major role in the structure and metabolism of the nervous system. The amounts of some of the more important lipid components are given in Table 23, containing data collected by McIlwain (41). The cholesterol of the brain in adult animals is apparently relatively inert metabolically as it does not exchange with that in other parts of the body. When D_2O is given to adult rats little deuterium enters the brain cholesterol but much is found in the cholesterol of liver and intestine (341). Moreover, little of the C^{14} from acetate-1-C^{14} enters the cholesterol of brain or spinal cord of adult rats. With the brain of *young* animals, however, there is incorporation of deuterium from D_2O, and C^{14} from acetate-1-C^{14}, into brain cholesterol. There seems to be little doubt that in the early stages of growth cholesterol is synthesized *in situ*. Once it is formed it is very stable and little turnover

TABLE 23

SOME LIPID COMPONENTS OF ADULT MAMMALIAN BRAIN

		Approximate amount as % of wet weight of brain	
		Grey Matter	*White Matter*
Cholesterol		1	4
Lecithin		1	1.4
Kephalins	Phosphatidylethanolamine	1.3	1.5
	Phosphatidylserine	0.5	2.1
	Diphosphoinositide	0.2	0.4
Sphingomyelin		0.5	2.0
Cerebrosides		0.9	4.8
Sulphatides		0.2	1.2
Gangliosides		0.07	0.14
Strandin		0.7	0.07

occurs over long periods of time Data quoted in a review of brain lipid metabolism by Rossiter (342), given in Table 24, show that C^{14} from acetate-1-C^{14} is incorporated in rat brain slices and cat sciatic nerve in a suitable physiological medium,

TABLE 24

LABELLING OF CHOLESTEROL FROM ACETATE-1-C^{14} IN TISSUE SLICES

	Specific activity of cholesterol c/min./mg.
Rat liver slices	170,000
Rat brain slices	300
Cat sciatic nerve	120

the rate being very much less than that in rat liver slices. Labelling of cholesterol was very much increased at the time of remyelination after injury had occurred to a nerve.

Various brain lipids are readily labelled from some precursors; for example, the fatty acid fraction of brain (unlike cholesterol) is labelled from D_2O in adult rats (341) and glycerol-1-C^{14} and glycerol-2-C^{14} are readily incorporated into the phosphatide fraction of brain (343). Moreover glycerol-1-C^{14} may be incorporated into the lipids (337), including the phosphatides (344) of brain slices. The evidence (342) indicates that the fatty acid moieties of the glycerophosphatides (IV-VI) are labelled from acetate, the glycerol moiety from glycerol, and the basic part from the base as such and not from glycerol.

When labelled fatty acids, or triglycerides, are given to animals, some labelling of brain phosphatides takes place. Labelled bases are also incorporated, but slowly, into brain phosphatides. N^{15} labelled choline or ethanolamine enters the brain constituents more slowly than in any other tissue studied (345). Probably most of these slow rates of incorporation are controlled by rates of penetration through the blood-brain barrier.

When brain slices are used, eliminating the blood-brain barrier, more rapid rates of metabolism may be observed and the course of the various changes more accurately studied.

Labelling by isotopic phosphate (P^{32}) of isolated brain lipids readily takes place (346), the synthesis needing oxidative metabolism in presence of glucose. Even in a brain homogenate (and also under anaerobic conditions) (347) P^{32} is incorporated into the lipids, the kephalin but not the lecithin fraction, but in brain slices there is negligible labelling under anaerobic conditions (346,348). Much of the P^{32} is incorporated into brain diphosphoinositide (VII) (349). The incorporation of inorganic P^{32} into ATP, either by oxidative or glycolytic phosphorylation, is probably the first step in the labelling of the immediate precursors of phos-

CH_3
|
$(CH_2)_{12}$
|
CH
||
CH
|
$CHOH$
|
$CHNH_2$
|
CH_2OH

Sphingosine
I

CH_3
|
$(CH_2)_{12}$
|
CH
||
CH
|
$CHOH$
|
$CH.NHCO \cdot (CH_2)_{22}CH_3$
|
$CH_2O-P \cdot O_2H-O \cdot CH_2 \cdot CH_2-N(CH_3)_3$

Sphingomyelin
II

CH_3
|
$(CH_2)_{12}$
|
CH
||
CH
|
$CHOH$
|
$CH.NH.CO \cdot (CH_2)_{22}CH_3$
|
$CH_2-O-Galactose$

Cerebroside (Kerasine)
III

$CH_2O-Acyl$
|
$CHO-Acyl$
|
$CH_2O.PO_2H.O \cdot CH_2CH_2N(CH_3)_3$

Lecithin
IV

$CH_2O-Acyl$
|
$CHO-Acyl$
|
$CH_2O.PO_2H.-O-CH_2CH_2NH_2$

Phosphatidylethanolamine
V

$CH_2O-Acyl$
|
$CHO-Acyl$
|
$CH_2O.PO_2H.-O-CH_2.CHNH_2$
|
$COOH$

Phosphatidylserine
VI

$CHOH-CH-PO_2 \cdot H.R$ R or R$'$ = Monoglyceride
| |
$CHOH$ $CHOH$
| |
$CHOH-CH-PO_2.H.R'$

Diphosphoinositide
VII

ɔholipids (350). A decrease in labelling of ATP, under a variety ɔf experimental conditions, leads to, or is associated with, a decrease of lipid P (351). It is likely that ATP, in addition to ts role as a precursor, is concerned in the energetics of phospho-ipid synthesis (505).

Application of acetylcholine (in presence of eserine) to guinea ɔig brain cortex slices causes an increase of lipid-P labelling ɔy P^{32} (337), the increase being abolished by the presence of atropine. The effect seemed to be located in the labelling of monophosphoinositide. Hokin and Hokin (353) conclude that 'the simplest hypothesis seems to be that acetylcholine stimulates the secretion of some complex molecule from certain cells of the brain cortex" for apparently increased *in vivo* labelling of phosphatides is associated with secretory processes. Diphosphoinositide undergoes rapid changes in brain tissues, two reactions being involved in its breakdown, a liberation of inositol monophosphate by a phosphodiesterase and a breakdown by a phosphomono esterase. Such reactions are possibly involved in sodium transport at the nerve cell membrane (508).

It is evident that the phosphatides of brain and peripheral nerve are in an active metabolic state, labelling by both *in vivo* and *in vitro* methods readily taking place. Much progress has been made in our knowledge of the details of phospholipid synthesis (354), some of the reactions involved being shown in Figure 2. It suffices here to emphasize the important roles of adenosine triphosphate, cytidine triphosphate and the magnesium dependent enzymes that control the rates of the various constituents leading to phospholipid synthesis.

Sphingomyelin (II), so named by Thudicum, which contains the base sphingosine (I) is a phosphocholine derivative, as is lecithin, and is of considerable interest in problems relating to brain dysfunction as it accumulates in abnormal amounts in brain and other organs in one of the familial lipidoses, while lecithins and kephalins are not so increased. It is known that the metabolism of glycine and serine contributes to the formation of sphingosine and that palmitaldehyde or palmityl-CoA is involved (355), but relatively little is known of sphingomyelin metabolism.

Glucose, or galactose, is incorporated into lipids (sphingolipids and mucolipids). Galactose is a better precursor than glucose for

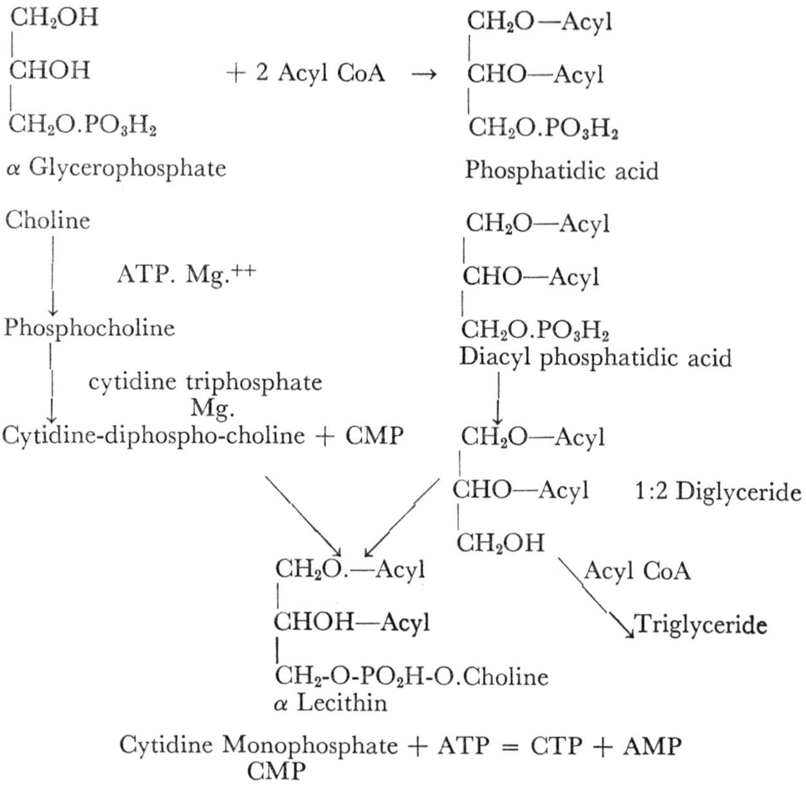

$$
\begin{array}{l}
CH_2OH \\
| \\
CHOH \qquad + 2\ Acyl\ CoA \quad \rightarrow \\
| \\
CH_2O.PO_3H_2
\end{array}
\qquad
\begin{array}{l}
CH_2O-Acyl \\
| \\
CHO-Acyl \\
| \\
CH_2O.PO_3H_2
\end{array}
$$

α Glycerophosphate ⟶ Phosphatidic acid

Choline

$\downarrow$ ATP. Mg.$^{++}$

Phosphocholine

$\downarrow$ cytidine triphosphate Mg.

Cytidine-diphospho-choline + CMP

$$
\begin{array}{l}
CH_2O-Acyl \\
| \\
CHO-Acyl \\
| \\
CH_2O.PO_3H_2 \\
\text{Diacyl phosphatidic acid} \\
\downarrow \\
CH_2O-Acyl \\
| \\
CHO-Acyl \qquad \text{1:2 Diglyceride} \\
| \\
CH_2OH
\end{array}
$$

$$
\begin{array}{l}
CH_2O.-Acyl \\
| \\
CHOH-Acyl \\
| \\
CH_2\text{-}O\text{-}PO_2H\text{-}O.Choline \\
\alpha\ Lecithin
\end{array}
\qquad
\begin{array}{l}
\searrow Acyl\ CoA \\
\\
\searrow Triglyceride
\end{array}
$$

Cytidine Monophosphate + ATP = CTP + AMP
CMP

Fig. 2

mucolipids, but the reverse is the case for other lipids. Labelled uridine diphosphogalactose (UDP-galactose) serves as a precursor for labelled lipid *in vitro* (356). Recent evidence (357) indicates that UDP-galactose donates its galactose to a suitable acceptor and finally radioactive cerebroside (III) is formed. Whether the acceptor is N-acylsphingosine, or sphingosine itself (to form O-galactosylsphingosine or psychosine), is not known though perhaps the latter alternative is correct (356).

Brief mention should be made of the neuraminic acid containing substances of the brain. Studies of the structure of brain ganglioside (that contains neuraminic acid) has led to the isolation of a gangliocerebroside (358) and substances of allied structure. It is possible that brain gangliosides are involved in neuronal membrane and transport functions.

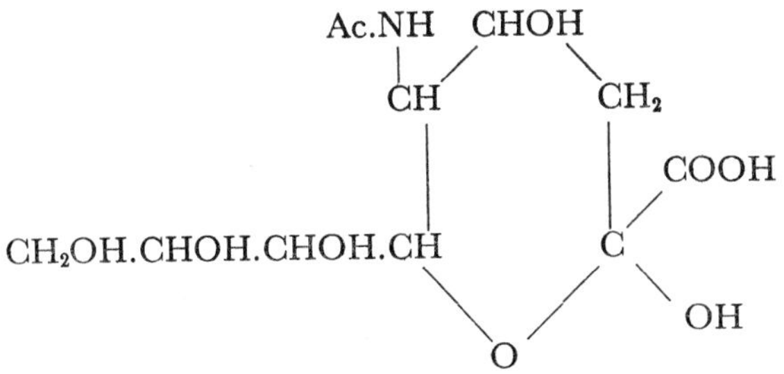

Ac.NH CHOH

CH CH₂

COOH

CH₂OH.CHOH.CHOH.CH C

OH

O

N-acetylneuraminic acid

Sphingolipids are almost exclusively constituents of the nerve sheaths and appear in myelination. They accumulate in the white matter of brain and spinal cord where they constitute almost half the total lipids.

NEUROLIPOIDOSES*

The following diseases are considered to be lipoidoses of the developing brain: the acute infantile form of Gaucher's disease, Niemann-Pick disease, amaurotic family iodiocy of the Tay-Sachs type, Pfaundler-Hurler's disease.

Gaucher's disease is regarded as being due to a disturbance of metabolism of the reticular tissue, the nervous tissue being involved usually only in the acute infantile form. There is extensive degeneration of the nerve cells. Most studies have been confined to the spleen, liver and lungs of patients with Gaucher's disease where the typical lipid-containing Gaucher cells are found in large numbers. The lipid stored in the typical Gaucher cells is thought to be a galactocerebroside. Thaunhauser *et al.* found both galacto- and gluco-cerebroside in the spleen of an infant with Gaucher's disease (360), but Klenk *et al.* found mainly glucocerebrosides in a number of patients; however with an infant having typical pathological changes of the brain only galactocerebrosides were found (359,361).

In Niemann-Pick disease, the nervous system stores sphingomyelin. This occurs also in the Pick cells in liver and spleen. There are, however, certain chemical differences between the fatty acid components of the sphingomyelin of different tissues.

*See 359,200

In the sphingomyelin of spleen and liver the unsaturated lignoceric acid occurs as well as palmitic and nervonic acids but in the brain sphingomyelin the saturated stearic acid predominates. Niemann-Pick disease occurs most frequently in infancy, the children dying within the first two years of life. There are, however, juvenile and adult forms of the disease. Some change in the enzymatic control of sphingomyelin synthesis in the formation of myelin presumably may account for the disorder but little is known about this.

In infantile amaurotic idiocy blindness due to optic nerve atrophy develops and idiocy coupled with complete paralysis takes place in about two years with a fatal result. The condition was first described by Tay and Sachs and Slome (362) who showed that the disease is controlled by a single recessive gene. It differs from the infantile form of Gaucher's and Niemann-Pick disease in that only the brain and nervous tissues are involved. Klenk et al. (361,359) found in cases of infantile amaurotic idiocy about ten to twenty times the normal content of gangliosides. The substances possess carbohydrate moieties containing galactosamine, chondrosamine, neuraminic acid and glucose. Stearic acid is the main constituent of the fatty acids present. Severe epilepsy usually occurs in this disorder.

Pfaundler-Hurler's disease (gargoylism) is often regarded as a special form of amaurotic familial idiocy, the disturbance in the development of the brain being accompanied by a disturbance in skeletal development. There seems to occur an increased production of gangliosides in the nerve cells and Brante (363) has observed that in tissues other than nervous tissue there seems to be an accumulation of a mucopolysaccharide related in structure to the carbohydrate group of the gangliosides. Klenk (359) considers that since mucopolysaccharides play an important role in skeletal composition there may be a connection between the disturbances of the skeleton and those of the nervous system.

The lipoidoses that have been mentioned are inherited disorders. They are metabolic aberrations controlled by genes. Little is known about the underlying causes of the metabolic disorders. Suggestions have been made that the essential features consist of the absence of specific esterases converting one lipid into another or of the absence, or deficiency, of appropriate coenzymes.

Evidently the diseases most frequently involve the metabolism of sphingomyelin and it is in this field of enquiry, so important for our knowledge of the constitution of the nerve cell and axon, that future advances may well be made.

GALACTOSEMIA

Although this disease, in which mental defect occurs, might more properly be considered under disorders of carbohydrate metabolism, it will be mentioned here because the mental defect may be due to interference with lipid metabolism. Galactose metabolism is involved in the formation of brain lipids. The disease is a recessive condition in which there is an inability to metabolize galactose normally. Clinical manifestations often appear within a few weeks after birth with vomiting, jaundice and loss of weight followed by retardation of physical and mental development, hepatomegaly and cataract. Blood galactose increases and oral administration of lactose or galactose results in a larger and persistent increase in blood galactose. About half the ingested galactose appears in the urine. Normally galactose is converted in the body into galactose-1-phosphate and then into uridine-diphosphogalactose. This then undergoes conversion to glucose. In galactosemia, the enzyme that accomplishes the change to the uridine diphosphogalactose (i.e., galactouridyl transferase) is missing (363). Galactose-1-phosphate accumulates in the tissues where it seems to be toxic. The reason for the association of the metabolic defect with the neurological symptoms is not clear. Restriction of galactose from the diet leads to improvement in symptoms and relief from mental deficiency. Even in patients aged one year some (though less) mental improvement may be achieved. There is evidence that galactose-1-phosphate can inhibit cell metabolism and its injection may cause convulsions. One suggestion (364) is that galactose-1-phosphate inhibits phosphoglucomutase, the enzyme that controls the conversion of glucose-1-phosphate to glucose-6-phosphate. It is, however, conceivable that it may interfere with galactose metabolism in the nervous system. Some of the symptomatology in the disease is probably due to hypoglycaemia (459). Blood glucose levels seem generally to be low when blood galactose is raised; this is true in normals as well as in patients with galactosaemia (460).

It is of interest to note that convulsions induced in isolated whole brain, in perfusion experiments (365), give rise to changes in brain galactolipids.

DEMYELINATION

The development of the myelin sheath (myelination) and its breakdown in pathological conditions (demyelination) are important processes that bear upon our understanding of the changes in Wallerian degradation and in such disorders as multiple sclerosis. The myelin sheath seems to consist of duplicated and infolded cell membranes (461). There is little doubt that studies of the mechanism of demyelination will be of value to the understanding of the chemistry and pathology of the glial and neuron membranes.

Demyelination has been studied in a variety of ways. Investigations have often been made of the substances, including tissue emulsions, that can produce demyelination in experimental animals or of the abnormal dietary conditions under which demyelination can take place. Demyelination, for example, occurs in lambs born of ewes maintained on a high intake of sulphate or of molybdate (506). All lambs showing ataxia and degenerative changes in the central nervous system had very low liver copper values. Studies have also been made of demyelination *in vitro* by the application of enzymes and of the chemical changes found in experimentally induced demyelination (notably Wallerian degeneration). Anoxia and respiratory poisons such as cyanide, sodium azide (520) and carbon monoxide on administration to animals give rise to demyelination. It would be expected that myelin synthesis would require the energy of oxidative processes and that interference with these would not only stop myelin synthesis but encourage breakdown mechanisms to operate. The administration of metabolic inhibitors such as fluoracetate, hydroxylamine and various narcotics in high quantity produce pathological lesions in the nervous system. These lesions, however, are not confined to white matter and are not primarily demyelinating (367,368). Many disorders exhibiting demyelination pathologically, such as nutritional deficiencies, subacute combined degeneration, amyotrophic lateral sclerosis, anoxic encephalopathy, and ischemic demyelination from vascular occlusions, are not regarded as demyelinating diseases because they have other pathological features considered more important than demyelination. Demyelination is a rather unspecific pathological finding and is probably a consequence of a variety of causes that interfere with metabolism in the white matter including nerve cell body destruction. Tetanus toxin and clostridium toxin, for example, induce demyelination. Triorthocresyl phosphate will produce this pathological change, particularly in chickens, and the possibility (369) has been considered that the pseudocholinesterase of nerve (which is inhibited by this ester) is involved in the maintenance of myelin sheaths of nerve fibres. Paralytic effects due to certain organo-phosphorus compounds, used as insecticides, may be partly due to pseudocholinesterase inhibition and possible accompanying demyelination.

ACUTE INTERMITTENT PORPHYRIA*

This disease of protean manifestations, that is inherited as an irregular dominant, is an "inborn error of metabolism" to be distinguished from "congenital" or erythropoietic porphyria, or the cutanea tarda type, neither of which is associated with neurological dysfunction. It is characterized by the excretion of large quantities of porphobilinogen and other porphyrin derivatives. There is no photosensitivity or discoloration of the bones and teeth. In the nervous system, there are widely scattered foci of demyelination which may be associated with limb paralysis, ataxia and nystagmus, or gross mental changes. Most commonly abdominal symptomatology is predominant. Acute attacks are precipitated by barbiturates, infections, and sometimes by pregnancy. It is postulated that there is a disorder of porphyrin metabolism in the liver and in the central nervous system, demyelination being the pathological expression. The effects of barbiturates on porphyrin metabolism and the role of the latter in myelination are unexplained.

VITAMIN B₁₂ DEFIENCY SYNDROME

Addisonian pernicious anaemia, according to current concepts, is a conditioned vitamin deficiency syndrome, due to absence of intrinsic factor secretion by the stomach, this factor being necessary for absorption of vitamin B₁₂. Neurological involvement is a

---

*See 521,471

prominent feature of the disease. Symptoms referable to peripheral polyneuropathy, posterolateral sclerosis of the spinal cord, optic atrophy, olfactory disturbances, memory loss, and psychosis may appear before anaemia is evident. While the anaemia can be corrected by pteroylglutamic acid (folic acid), such treatment does not benefit the neurological dysfunction, and can exacerbate it (366).

It seems evident that vitamin B_{12} is essential for the metabolic processes concerned with the functional integrity of myelinated nerve fibers. Treatment with it can cause a remarkable remission in symptomatology, in cases of this disease, though much of the pathology is irreversible (522).

According to Williams et al. (472) the vitamin is necessary as a cofactor, or cofactor precursor, for transmethylation reactions and the metabolism of labile methyl groups but whether this fact bears upon the neurological symptoms of vitamin B_{12} deficiency is still unknown.

SWAYBACK OR ENZOOTIC ATAXIA

The importance of nutritional factors in the process of demyelination has been emphasized by Rossiter (267). The well known demyelinating condition of newborn lambs termed *swayback* or enzootic ataxia is associated with low concentrations of copper in the pasture and in the blood and liver of the parent ewe and of the affected lamb (370). Feeding small amounts of copper prevents development of the condition. It is inferred that copper plays an important role in the process of myelination and that demyelination may be caused by interference with certain enzymic processes associated with copper. There is no evidence, however, that copper deficiency plays any role in multiple sclerosis.

Phospholipid synthesis in liver is known to be much affected by the changes induced by copper deficiency, and liver mitochondria of animals kept on a copper deficient diet show far less respiratory activity than those prepared from a normal animal (371). It seems very likely that copper ions are involved in the metabolic events that lead to myelination and demyelination.

PHOSPHOLIPID STRUCTURE AND BRAIN METABOLISM

The possible role of lecithinase (phospholipase A) and lysolecithin in the neurological symptoms produced by venoms was first suggested by Houssay et al. (372), and Morrison and Zamecnik

(373) have in fact suggested that lysolecithin, if formed in the central nervous system, may produce a local demyelination. Exposure of spinal cord or brain to cobra venom or to the alpha toxin of *Cl. welchii* (phospholipase C) results in demyelination. Phosphosphingoside which is present in the myelin sheath is also hydrolyzed by phospholipase C. Venoms that have been heated to destroy all enzymes but the phospholipase A retain about half their original toxicity and produce, on administration to the animal, marked lesions in the nervous system (377). Recent results (374) show that the presence of venom phospholipase A will form lysolecithin from mitochondrial lecithin and has inhibitory effects on oxidative processes in brain cortex slices similar to those in brain mitochondria or brain homogenates (375). It was concluded (374) that the first effect of phospholipase A on mitochondrial metabolism is a release of protein with a fall in the rate of oxidative phosphorylations, phenomena that would be the result of an attack on phospholipids in the mitochondrial structure. Brain cell membranes, as well as those in brain mitochondria, contain phospholipid groups that are attacked by phospholipase and which control metabolic events associated with the membranes. The role of lipids in electron transport, or respiratory mechanisms, is now the subject of many investigations (e.g., 376) and there is little doubt that the destructive effect of phospholipases on tissue respiratory processes is due to the removal of lipids essential for oxidative phosphorylations and for the integrity of mitochondrial structure. The phospholipids are not only important as structural elements of brain cells, but they are essential for the maintenance of normal oxidative metabolism. Interference with their composition, and release of lysolecithin, will be expected to produce local changes in metabolism, that will become more extensive as interference with oxidative metabolism progresses.

WALLERIAN DEGENERATION

The chemistry of myelin breakdown that accompanies Wallerian degeneration has been extensively studied. This pathological condition is characterized, at first, by physical disintegration of the myelin sheath with but little breakdown of the myelin lipids (378). There are marked changes in metabolism (e.g., failure of the nerve to synthesize acetycholine, and nucleic acid changes) and loss of ability of the nerve to conduct an impulse. There then takes place a rapid disappearance of myelin lipids with parallel enzymatic changes and altered nucleic acid components and finally the myelin sheath almost entirely disappears, the Schwann cells occupying the spaces left by the degenerated sheath and axon. It is possible (367) that the destruction of myelin that takes place in the degenerating nerve is due to an enzyme system derived from a type of cell which is present in large numbers during the degeneration process. Two types of cell may be responsible: one is the macrophage, the other the proliferating Schwann cell. McCaman and Robins (500), studying qualitative biochemical changes in rabbit tibial and optic nerves undergoing Wallerian degeneration, point out that the lipid changes (501) and enzymatic changes (502) proceed at different rates in the two nerves and suggest that the Schwann cells and macrophages in the peripheral nervous system are more effective in the removal of myelin than the glial cells and the macrophages of the central nervous system.

STEROIDS

Evidence is accumulating that steroids may play a significant role in the control of brain metabolism and function. Severe adrenal insufficiency is accompanied by slowing of electrical discharges in the brain as seen in the E.E.G., a normal pattern being restored by administration of cortisone (379). In the rat, changes in E.E.G. due to adrenalectomy revert to normal with replacement therapy. These changes are correlated with changes in rates of blood flow and oxygen utilization (380). Effects of steroids on electrolyte content in the brain are reported (384,385). For example, the exchange rate of potassium in the brain is affected by adrenalectomy (385).

Cerebral dysfunction often accompanies hormonal disturbances as in diseases of the thyroid, adrenals and pancreas. Hypopituitarism and adult eunuchism are characterized by a sluggish rate of cerebral oxygen consumption (389). The data seem to demonstrate hormonal control of cerebral metabolism. Therapy with commonly used adrenal steroids and their derivatives seems generally to be associated with mental changes, usually euphoria but occasionally of a more serious nature, including psychotic breakdown. These phenomena are not interpretable on the basis of an obvious biochemical change. It is reported (462) that in such individuals exhibiting neuropsychiatric symptoms the E.E.G. shows abnormal slow wave activity and a reduction of basic alpha activity.

Experiments with rats (463) have demonstrated profound effects of steroids on the central nervous system, including long lasting convulsions (compound S), synergism with many anaesthetic drugs (hydrocortisone) or anaesthetic activity *per se* (desoxycortico-sterone).

Various steroids affect the oxygen consumption of brain slices in normal physiological media. This applies to desoxycortico-sterone, dehydroandrosterone and testosterone (381). There is a parallelism between the anaesthetic action of certain steroids (382) and their capacities to depress oxygen consumption of brain preparations in presence of glucose (383).

Steroids have high affinities for components in brain tissue and the 3-ketosteroids can affect dehydrogenase systems. Diethyl stilbestrol, which has certain features in common with steroids, can act as a hydrogen carrier in the cell (386), in virtue of the reaction

$$\text{quinol} \leftrightharpoons \text{quinone}$$

It is now known that estrogenic steroids such as estradiol-17β can mediate the transfer of hydrogen between TPN and DPN (387). This is brought about by the fact that the enzyme involved catalyses both the reduction of the two nucleotides by estradiol and the oxidation of the reduced forms by estrone. New work (388) shows that both natural and synthetic phenolic estrogens can act as biological hydrogen carriers in two types of reactions (a) catalysis by phenolases, involving apparently an initial hydroxylation of the estrogen to a corresponding o-diphenol, the change, diphenol $\leftrightharpoons$ quinone, taking place, and (b) catalysis by a free peroxidase, implicating a free radical form of the estrogen as a hydrogen carrier. Thus, it is apparent that certain classes of steroids can, in presence of appropriate enzymes, affect the DPN and TPN linked systems, acting as hydrogen carriers that must form part of the complex of hydrogen transporting systems that help to establish the over-all metabolic steady state.

Whilst it is too early to conclude that the physiological activities of steroid hormones are linked with reactions such as those described, the fact that steroids are known to affect metabolic events in the brain, and, being highly lipid soluble, would have access to nervous structures, it seems possible that such metabolic interference will play a role in their effects on the nervous system. The important "feed-back" action of cortisone on ACTH release by the pituitary may be due to an action of this steroid on the metabolism of appropriate cells in the pituitary body or hypothalamus.

EFFECTS OF HYPNOTICS, ANAESTHETICS, TRANQUILIZERS ON BRAIN METABOLISM

In the hope of throwing light on the mode of action of anaesthetics in the body and on a possible relationship between biochemical changes in the central nervous system and the narcotic state, experiments were carried out in 1932 on the effects of hypnotics and anaesthetics on brain respiratory systems (390). As a result of these and many succeeding investigations it is known that narcotics, with the exception of morphine and allied substances, are able to inhibit the respiration of isolated brain tissue in presence of glucose or pyruvate, especially if this is examined in the form of brain slices or brain mitochondria. This conclusion applies also to local anaesthetics, to chlorpromazine and to the steroid anaesthetics. There is in fact a close correlation among narcotics and anaesthetics of different chemical types between hypnotic activity and respiratory inhibition. The high sensitivity to narcotics and anaesthetics of glucose oxidation in the brain is a striking feature of narcotic action *in vitro*. Such observations made it seem possible that the interference with brain function, accomplished by narcotics and allied substances, is related to changed metabolic events in the nerve cell as a result of the presence of the drug. The concentrations of narcotics required to accomplish inhibitory effects on neuronal metabolism were, however, so large compared with those required to induce narcosis that the affected reactions were thought to have no relation to the narcotic state. This conclusion is now untenable because further work has made it clear that narcotics at low pharmacological concentrations bring about two phenomena, which are not, however, necessarily independent:

1. Suppression of that aspect of neuronal respiration which has been stimulated by increased potassium ion concentration (392) (or increased K^+/Ca^{++}), or by application of electrical impulses (393).

2. Uncoupling of phosphorylation from oxidative processes (394) (a phenomenon not always observed, however, with brain mitochondria) followed by a depressing effect on total oxygen consumption.

In view of what has been described earlier of the properties of brain tissue stimulated *in vitro*, by changed electrolyte concentration or by application of electric impulses, and of the approximation of the behaviour of such excited tissue *in vitro* to that of functioning brain, the new results on the effects of narcotics *in vitro* have an obvious physiological significance (523).

Such results do not, of course, imply that all nerve cells in the brain are equally affected by the drug when it causes anaesthesia or narcosis or mental changes, nor that a depression of total brain respiration should necessarily ensue. They do imply, however, that the affected cells can no longer carry on their normal biochemical, and functional, behaviour and, therefore, that those parts of the nervous system controlled by the activities of the affected cells will also be affected, with resulting effects on the nervous system as a whole that will vary according to the location and neurophysiological significance of the affected cells.

There has been ample demonstration of reduced respiration *in vivo* in the central nervous system during the narcosis brought about by a variety of drugs. Himwich *et al.* (22) have found that, under pentothal, oxygen consumption of the cerebral cortex is decreased more than that of the lower centres. With thiopental anaesthesia the average oxygen uptake is lowered about 35%. According to Shaw *et al.* (396) ether anaesthesia is associated with a decrease in the difference between the oxygen contents of arterial and venous bloods. Dameshek *et al.* (397) have shown that in the human subject under the influence of amytal there is a small but definite inhibition of oxygen uptake and glucose utilization by the brain. The depression of cerebral function by barbiturates indeed parallels the reduction of oxygen uptake. This fall in oxygen uptake *in vivo*, however, it is important to emphasize, may only be a reflection of the diminished cerebral activity obtained during narcosis. It does not, itself, point to an interference with respiratory activity of the nerve cells by the responsible drugs.

Narcotics and anaesthetics do not inhibit *in vitro* all oxidative processes to the same extent, nor have they any effect at low concentrations on most dehydrogenases. They do not inhibit, for example, brain glycolysis, a process that involves the interplay of various dehydrogenase systems (398). Indeed there is ample evidence to indicate that narcotics actually increase aerobic glycolysis by suppression of the Pasteur effect. Possibly this is the explanation for the observation (399) that narcotics, at low concentration, accelerate glucose consumption by exised rat superior cervical ganglia, a conclusion in conformity with a variety of observations (400) that in the presence of narcotics there is an increased rate of breakdown of glucose despite a suppression of oxygen uptake.

The large effects of low concentrations of narcotics on cationic stimulated respiration of brain slices in presence of radioactive glucose, in which measurements of formation of radioactive carbon dioxide are made, are shown in Table 25 (87).

TABLE 25

Effects of Amytal and Doriden on $C^{14}O_2$ Formation from Glucose-U-C^{14}
(10 mM; 10^5 c/m) in Presence of Rat Brain Cortex Slices
$C^{14}O_2$ Values Given as Counts/min./mg. Tissue

	No drug added	Amytal 0.5 mM	Doriden 2.5 mM	10 mM
$C^{14}O_2$ evolved in 90 mins.				
K^+ = 5 meq./l.	211	145	217	200
K^+ = 105 meq./l	528	165	416	179
% inhibition by drug of stimulated $C^{14}O_2$ output	94		26	100

The narcotic concentration of Doriden (α ethyl α phenylglutarimide) for the rat = 700 mg./kilo.;
The LD$_{50}$ of Amytal (5 ethyl 5 isoamyl barbituric acid) for the rat = 115 mg Kg. rat

It is in accordance with the conclusion (398) that anaesthetics suppress specifically at low concentrations the activity of a process playing an intermediate part in tissue respiration between cytochrome oxidase and a flavoprotein involving DPN that Amytal (5-ethyl-5-isoamylbarbiturate) is a highly effective inhibitor of the oxidation of reduced DPN and its associated phosphorylations (401), thus:

$$DPNH_2 + ADP + P_i \quad \underset{\substack{\text{inhibited} \\ \text{by Amytal}}}{\overset{O}{\rightarrow}} \quad DPN + ATP + H_2O$$

The suppression of DPNH$_2$ oxidation by Amytal has the double effect of suppressing the citric acid cycle (as pyruvate oxidation requires DPN for its conversion to acetyl-CoA) and ATP formation.

The interference of narcotics with ATP synthesis in the brain is shown by their suppression of acetylcholine synthesis (402) and by their inhibitory effects (e.g. those of 4 mM chloretone or 1 mM Nembutal) on P^{32} incorporation (from phosphate) into phosphoproteins and organic phosphorus compounds in cat brain slices respiring in presence of glucose (403). A striking demonstration of the effect of a low concentration of a narcotic (Amytal) on ATP formation in brain slices is shown by its action in suppressing glutamine synthesis, a reaction that requires the participation of ATP in the condensation of glutamate and ammonia. Results illustrating this phenomenon are shown in Table 26 (88),

TABLE 26

INFLUENCE OF 0.5 mM SODIUM AMYTAL ON RADIOACTIVE AMINO ACID FORMATION FROM GLUCOSE-U-C^{14} IN PRESENCE OF RAT BRAIN CORTEX SLICES (GLUCOSE-U-C^{14} = 5 MM; 10^6 C/M. AEROBIC CONDITION. K$^+$ = 105 MEQ./1.)

Amino acid values expressed as counts/min./100 mg. wet weight tissue.		
Amino acid formed	No amytal added	Amytal 0.5 mM
Glutamic acid	5516 ± 475	6761 ± 450
Aspartic acid	1183 ± 185	661 ± 51
Glutamine	2397 ± 209	111 ± 10
Alanine	794 ± 49	386 ± 36
γ Aminobutyric acid	1491 ± 164	1479 ± 123

where it is obvious that a very large fall in the yield of labelled glutamine from labelled glucose occurs. Other changes also take place and these can be satisfactorily explained by the conclusion that Amytal has a two-fold effect (a) diminution of DPN formation from DPNH$_2$ and (b) diminution of ATP formation (88). TPNH$_2$ oxidation in brain is apparently not affected by Amytal (515). Transhydrogenase, that links DPN with TPN, is absent from brain (516).

When the respiration of rat and guinea brain slices is stimulated electrically it becomes more sensitive to the action of barbiturates, chloral and mescaline (404). Chlorpromazine at low concentrations reduces the enhanced respiration due to electrical excitation (405) just as it reduces the increased oxygen uptake found with potassium ion stimulation (65). It also brings about some inhibition *in vitro* of incorporation of glycine-1-C^{14} into rat brain cortex proteins, a process that is ATP dependent, at concentrations (0.2 mM) that have little or no effect on the respiration of brain or on the breakdown of glycine-1-C^{14} into $C^{14}O_2$ (65). Thus it is possible that chlorpromazine may affect physiological action by an uncoupling action on ATP synthesis at the particular site in the brain where it gains access most easily to the relevant enzyme systems. The addition of chlorpromazine (at 0.1 mM) to guinea pig brain slices brings about changes in labelling of lipid phosphorus in presence of P^{32}, namely decreases of phosphatidylethanolamine and phosphatidylcholine and increase of phosphoinositide; with higher concentrations of the drug there is a considerable decrease in labelling of lipid phosphorus (406).

Recent results (490) indicate that chlorpromazine uncouples phosphorylations coupled to the oxidation of ferrocytochrome C and inhibits DPNH-cytochrome C reductase, the effect being mainly due to an effect on the coupled phosphorylation reaction.

It is not known yet if steroid inhibitions of metabolism are affected by stimulation of the brain though it is evident that steroid hormones interfere with tissue oxidations. Recent evidence (407) shows that the site of action of corticosterone, and possibly other steroid hormones, lies in the respiration chain between the flavoproteins and cytochrome c, a site already suggested as the point of action of many narcotics (398).

Inhibitive effects of narcotics, anaesthetics, or a tranquiliser such as chlorpromazine, on ATP synthesis in the brain do not necessarily involve immediate falls in respiration in the brain cells affected. A situation may arise where the increased concentration of ADP, which, as has been explained earlier, has a rate limiting effect on metabolic reactions involved in glucose breakdown, can give rise to an increased rate of oxygen consumption. This is a frequent effect of the addition of respiratory "uncouplers." Nevertheless this affect may be transient, depending on a variety of conditions, and the ultimate effect of suppression of so important a process as $DPNH_2$ oxidation must be a suppression of respiration.

The effects of these drugs on oxidative synthesis of ATP and, therefore, on the synthesis of acetylcholine, especially that bound in subcellular particles, to be drawn upon during the functional activity of the nerve cell, might account for a diminished rate of recovery of the cell to its normal condition. This slowing of recovery rate may well be a dominant factor in causing paralysis of the nerve cell or centres specifically affected by the drugs.

Narcotics, such as pentobarbital and ethanol, exercise a larger percentage depression of respiration in the adult than the young rat brain (409), a result that is to be expected on the evidence, already mentioned, that the activity of the citric acid cycle increases with age during the early days of post natal life and that the effects of K^+ on aerobic nerve metabolism is greatly decreased in infant animal brain. There is a significant positive correlation between rate of respiration at different ages, and sensitivity to barbiturates (497). Apparently in old age the inhibitory effects of barbiturates on respiration diminish, the maximum effects occurring in the young adult.

EFFECTS OF CHLORPROMAZINE ON BRAIN METABOLISM *IN VITRO*

Chlorpromazine also exerts an inhibitory activity on the respiration of brain cortex slices in presence of glucose, pyruvate or L-glutamate but not with succinate. This inhibitory effect is greatly increased with brain cortex slices stimulated by the presense of potassium ions, a definite inhibition occuring with 0.2 mM chlorpromazine. Moreover, the drug diminishes the incorporation of labelled glycine into brain proteins during incubation of brain cortex slices in a glucose-Ringer medium. This inhibition is associated with reduction of ATP required for amino acid incorporation into proteins. The effect is also brought about by Amytal and ethanol at low concentrations (Table 27).

TABLE 27

Effects of Chlorpromazine and Amytal on Glycine-1-C[14] Incorporation Into Rat Brain Cortex Proteins (65,523) After Aerobic Incubation in a Saline-phosphate-glucose Medium

Drug	Concentration	Percentage inhibition of glycine incorporation
Chlorpromazine	0.2 mM	20
	0.3 mM	30
Amytal	0.1 mM	4
	0.5 mM	55
Ethanol	0.4 M	53

Thus chlorpromazine, like Amytal, brings about an apparent uncoupling of phosphorylation from brain cortex respiration. However, the action of chlorpromazine *in vitro* differs from that of the barbiturates in bringing about progressive inhibitions and in its high binding power with tissue proteins (probably lipoproteins). The drug after combining with tissue components gradually diffuses into the brain cell bringing about its metabolic inhibitions (65). The conclusion that chlorpromazine, like Amytal, affects $DPNH_2$ oxidation (in phosphorylating systems such as those in brain cortex *in vitro*) has recently been confirmed with the use of liver mitochondrial systems (456), where it was also shown that 0.2 mM chlorpromazine brings about a marked inhibition of incorporation of P^{32} into ATP. The suggestion was made that the chlorpromazine effect is mainly located on the coupled phosphorylation reaction. These facts do not imply that chlorpromazine and Amytal act at the same locations in the nervous system. It is possible, in fact, that the differences between the clinical effects of these two drugs are due more to their different sites of action than to differences in biochemical mechanism.

Analyses of brain tissue taken from animals during narcosis show levels of ATP higher than those in the normal brain. Experiments, reported by Bain (408), show also that injection of P^{32} into mice during Amytal or thiopental narcosis leads to increased quantities of P^{32} being incorporated into ATP of mouse brain. It is possible to understand this effect if it is considered that with decreased cerebral activity following the inhibition of certain activating centres by the narcotic, there is a lessened stimulation of nerve cells in many parts of the brain (not directly affected by the drug) with a smaller rate of ADP formation. It has been shown earlier that stimulation of brain leads to increased ADP production. It follows that higher values of ATP in the brain following narcosis are a reflection of lessened cerebral activity, or lessened nerve stimulation, consequent upon the paralysis of nerve cells in special regions, or even very highly localized sites, of the brain.

It is of interest to note that succinate, whose oxidation in the brain is apparently not affected by narcotics or mescaline has a definite antidotal effect on mescaline psychosis (493,494,495), the effect not being due to bicarbonate formation or enhanced peripheral mescaline breakdown.

Alcohols and Brain Metabolism

Recent investigations (392,410) have shown that the addition of ethanol at small concentrations diminish the oxygen consumption of rat brain cortex slices respiring in a glucose-phosphate medium when this has been stimulated by the presence of 100 meq./l. K^+. Potassium stimulated respiration of rat brain slices is much more affected by ethanol at low concentration than the normal respiration, the concentration being of the same order as that necessary to bring about the narcotic state in the rat. The behaviour of ethanol is similar in this respect to that brought about by anaesthetics such as the barbiturates or chloretone. These results have been confirmed by Fischer (411), Sutherland et al. (413) and more recently by Wallgren and Kulonen (496), who have also shown that ethanol causes a decrease in the respiration of electrically stimulated brain tissue in presence of glucose.

The inhibitory effects of the alcohols increase markedly as the length of the carbon chain increases and with increase of their concentration, and the potassium ion stimulation of brain cortex respiration is diminished or abolished by concentrations of alcohols that have little effect on the unstimulated respiration (410). n-Pentanol is much more effective than ethanol in effecting an inhibition of the stimulated respiration and there seems to take place a rapid establishment of equilibria between the alcohols and the components that influence the brain respiratory system. In confirmation of the results of Wolpert et al. (414), it has been found (410) that brain mitochondrial respiration is relatively insensitive to concentrations of alcohols that considerably depress stimulated rat brain slice respiration. In this respect, the alcohols differ from the barbiturates and their effects resemble those of chlorpromazine (415). The results support the conclusion that the alcohols exercise their inhibitory effects on brain respiration at some site located in the brain cell membranes. If this is true, it must be concluded that a significant proportion of the brain cell respiration is controlled by the cell membrane where presumably the potassium ion stimulation takes place. The alternative explanations that the alcohols are oxidized to the highly toxic aldehydes (410) or that the alcohols block the entry of substrates into the cell have been ruled out.

The narcotics, including anaesthetics, belong to many structural types such as hydrocarbons, alcohols, ethers, urethanes, barbiturates, steroids and gases such as nitrous oxide. Their common property of inducing narcosis must depend on physico-chemical characters they have in common. Their affinities for lipids have long been a subject for discussion and investigation, and these are no doubt partly responsible for their penetration of the blood-brain barrier and subsequent narcotic effects. It seems most probable that the narcotics influence both mitochondrial and nerve cell respiration, by their adsorption or combination with lipid groups present in the membranes, these groups being involved in the establishment of ionic gradients and respiratory metabolism of the cell. Breakdown of phospholipid groups at the membrane brings about, as its first effect, an uncoupling of phosphorylation from respiration (a fall in P/O ratio). It is not, therefore, unreasonable to assume that the attachment of narcotics to such groups will also lead to the same result i.e.: interference with electron transport and oxidative phosphorylation. This results in a suppression of the functional activities of the cell. This concept of the mode of action of narcotics, which links the physico-chemical characters of the drugs with their effects on oxidative processes makes it possible to relate their metabolic effects to their established physical attributes embraced in the classical Overton-Meyer hypothesis.

BILIRUBIN ENCEPHALOPATHY

A substance that resembles narcotics in its ability to interfere with mitochondrial oxidative phosphorylation is bilirubin (416). The normal pathway of bilirubin detoxication is by conjunction with glucuronic acid followed by excretion of the glucuronide in the bile. Sometimes, however, the rate of bilirubin production exceeds that of its removal, as in haemolytic disease, or when the liver conjugates the bilirubin at a rate much lower than the normal, as in premature infants. It has been pointed out (416) that, in such cases, regardless of the aetiology of the hyperbilirubinemia a syndrome of severe brain damage may develop, called kernicterus, or bilirubin encephalopathy, if the serum bilirubin level is more than 20 mg. per cent. Bilirubin is a very effective inhibitor of oxidative phosphorylation *in vitro* accomplishing its effects at concentrations that do not affect the rate of total oxygen consumption. That it can affect ATP formation in the intact cell is shown by the observation that bilirubin greatly inhibits at small concentrations (0.16 mM) amino acid incorporation into proteins in ascites carcinoma cells (277). It is possible that the brain damage caused by bilirubin is due to a phenomenon of this sort.

The high serum bilirubin in congenital non hemolytic jaundice is likely to be due to a failure of the enzymes normally present in the liver microsomes to bring about conjugation of bilirubin with glucuronic acid by way of the coenzyme uridine-diphospho-glucuronic acid (417).

There is much circumstantial evidence that the neonatal blood-brain barrier is more permeable to various substances than the mature blood-brain barrier. It has been suggested that the blood-brain barrier in haemolytic diseases is affected by immunological processes (464), to explain the fact that the levels of bilirubinaemia necessary to cause kernicterus are not as high in erythroblastotic infants as in non-erythroblastotic.

Odell (465) has postulated that the incidence of kernicterus is related not to the total concentration of bilirubin in the circulation but only to that amount which is freely diffusible and not bound to the serum albumin. Whereas usually these figures are proportional many substances including sulfonamides and haematin seem to reduce the binding of bilirubin to albumin, thus permitting increased bilirubin staining of tissues. Low serum albumin levels would have the same effect. This may provide an explanation for the occurrence in premature infants of kernicterus associated with fairly low concentrations of bilirubin in the plasma.

It is also notable that in infants with hyperbilirubinemia there is some degree of hepatic dysfunction. This may entail some impairment of energy metabolism in the brain. Consequent failure to maintain impermeability of the nerve cell membrane could lead to staining by bilirubin and to irreversible damage (418).

Effects of Ions, Organic Bases and Drugs on Brain Metabolism

It has already been pointed out (p. 11) that cationic balance greatly affects the course of aerobic metabolism in isolated brain cortex. Anaerobic carbohydrate metabolism is also affected by the K^+/Ca^{++} ratio (p. 34). It has been shown, however (169), that a number of organic bases, notably pyrrole, quinoline, p-chloraniline and pyridine, accelerate anaerobic brain slice glycolysis in a calcium free medium, the concentrations needed for optimal activity varying considerably e.g. pyrrole 32 mM; quinoline 1.6 mM. The effects of the organic bases cannot be explained in terms of DPN-ase inhibitions; they seem, in some manner, to replace calcium ions at the brain cell membrane. Results of physiological tests showed (169) that the organic bases, pyrrole, quinoline and p-chloraniline exert neuro-physiological effects simulating those of calcium ions in abolishing the spontaneous firing of cat cervical sympathetic ganglia but there was no restoration of sympathetic transmission. New membrane equilibria are established in the presence of the bases, reflected on the one hand by changed rates of glucose breakdown in the brain cell and on the other by changed neurophysiological activities. The neurone membrane is an important rate limiting factor in cellular glucose metabolism, both under aerobic and anaerobic conditions. Changes in equilibria at the neurone surface, leading to increased rates of anaerobic glycolysis may, be secured by varying the external ionic balance (in which certain organic cations may replace the inorganic) or by increasing the surface $DPN/DPNH_2$ ratio (169).

The fact that a drug may exert a neurophysiological action by an effect on the cationic balance at the nerve cell membrane is indicated by results obtained with protoveratrine and cocaine (475).

Wollenberger (476) has demonstrated that addition of protoveratrine (well known for its excitation of muscle and nervous tissue) to guinea pig brain cortex slices brings about large increases of the respiratory rate and of the rate of aerobic glycolysis. Protoveratrine, like increased K^+, accelerates the rates of oxygen consumption of brain cortex in presence of glucose, lactate or pyruvate but not in presence of succinate. Moreover, like increased K^+, it is not effective with brain homogenates. Protoveratrine stimulation of rat brain cortex respiration in presence of glucose, like that due to increased K^+, is highly sensitive to narcotics and to malonate.

Results given in Table 28 show that the addition of $5 \times 10^{-6}\ M$ protoveratrine to rat brain cortex slices incubated aerobically in presence of glucose-U-C^{14} gives rise to a radioactive amino acid

TABLE 28

Effects of Protoveratrine and Cocaine on Radioactive Amino Acid Formation
from Glucose-U-C^{14} in Presence of Rat Brain Cortex Slices (475)
Glucose $= 5$ mM; KCl $= 5$ mM; CaCl$_2$ $= 3.6$ mM

Radioactive values given as c/min./100 mg. wet weight tissue/10^6 c/min. glucose-U-C^{14}	Protoveratrine 5 μM	Cocaine 0.5 mM	Protoveratrine 5 μM + Cocaine 0.5 mM	No drugs added
Glutamic acid	7869 ± 276	5928 ± 569	5845 ± 92	5565 ± 172
Glutamine	1957 ± 105	1365 ± 96	1079 ± 97	1302 ± 92
Gamma Aminobutyric acid	1832 ± 56	795 ± 20	739 ± 22	966 ± 57
Aspartic acid	1727 ± 56	1751 ± 65	1541 ± 59	1353 ± 59
Alanine	631 ± 65	744 ± 42	826 ± 25	721 ± 52
O$_2$ uptake cmm/100 mg.	234 ± 6.4	158 ± 8.2	152 ± 7.3	194 ± 5.3

pattern, which differs from that obtained in the absence of protoveratrine. The difference consists largely of increased yields of
labelled glutamic acid, glutamine and γ-aminobutyric acid,
a phenomenon characteristic of the effects of increased K$^+$ (88,
475). Effects of increased K$^+$ on the amino acid pattern under
similar experimental conditions are shown in Table 17. The
changes in the relative yields of labelled amino acids brought
about by the addition of the protoveratine resemble, however,
more closely the effects obtained when the brain cortex slices are
incubated in the Ringer medium from which calcium ions have
been removed. Results describing these effects are given in Table
29. The effects of increased K$^+$ in presence of 3.6 mM CaCl$_2$,
and of absence of Ca^{++} in presence of normal K$^+$ (5 mM KCl),
are similar but not identical, indicating that although the primary
change is due to the increased ratio K$^+$/Ca^{++}, secondary effects
of these ions take place. It has been shown (88) that the major

TABLE 29

Effects of Cocaine (0.5 mM) on Radioactive Amino Acid Formation
from Glucose-U-C^{14} in Presence of Rat Brain Cortex Slices
and in Absence of Ca^{++} (475)
Glucose $= 5$ mM; CaCl$_2$ $=$ Nil

Radioactive values given as c/min./100 mg. wet weight tissue/10^6 c/min. glucose-U-C^{14}	KCl 5 mM	Cocaine 0.5 mM + KCl 5 mM
Glutamic acid	9280 ± 365	6846 ± 569
Glutamine	1762 ± 97	1233 ± 58
Gamma Aminobutyric acid	1669 ± 94	1301 ± 23
Aspartic acid	2123 ± 65	2003 ± 173
Alanine	955 ± 34	1086 ± 42
O$_2$ uptake cmm/100 mg. wet weight tissue	232 ± 2.1	176 ± 6.4

change, the increased labelling of the amino acids, may be attributed to an acceleration of the conversion of pyruvate to acetyl-CoA by increased K^+/Ca^{++}. The effects of addition of 5 μM protoveratrine, in a normal Ringer medium, may be satisfactorily explained if the effect of protoveratrine consists of immobilization of, or competition with, Ca^{++}, resulting in a virtual increase of the ratio of K^+/Ca^{++}. However, a similar result would be obtained if the protoveratrine affected the relative permeabilities to Na^+ and K^+ in the brain cortex, so as to yield, in effect, an increased ratio of K^+/Ca^{++} in the extracellular medium. It is well known (477) that the veratrine alkaloids bring about marked changes in ion permeability and bioelectric phenomena and it has been suggested (478,479) that veratrine and Ca^{++} compete for sites on the cell surface. Gershfeld and Shanes (481) have indeed demonstrated a model (monolayers of stearic acid) in which there occurs a competition between veratrine and Ca^{++} for carboxyl groups in the fatty acid film.

It is evident that the action of protoveratrine on metabolic changes in brain cortex *in vitro* may be satisfactorily explained by its neurophysiological effect i.e. antagonism for Ca^{++}.

If this view is correct, it may be expected that the known neurophysiological antagonism between protoveratrine and cocaine (477,482) will be reflected by an antagonism in their metabolic effects.

The results (Table 28) demonstrate that the addition of cocaine (0.5 mM) to rat brain cortex slices incubated in a normal Ringer medium brings about a fall in respiratory activity with relatively little change in the pattern of labelled amino acids derived from glucose-U-C^{14} (475). The addition, however, of cocaine to protoveratrine, in presence of the rat brain cortex slices, not only suppresses the stimulation of respiratory rate due to protoveratrine, but causes a marked change in the amino acid pattern, reducing the increased labelling of glutamic acid, glutamine and γ-aminobutyric acid to approximately the same levels found with cocaine alone. This result is to be correlated with the known effect of cocaine in reducing the action of veratrine on ionic exchange and is consistent with the conclusion that cocaine (0.5 mM) acts in a manner similar to Ca^{++}, its presence resulting in an effective diminution of the ratio K^+/Ca^{++} at the brain cell surface.

The latter conclusion may be put to a further test by examining the effects of cocaine (0.5 mM) on the metabolic activities of rat brain cortex slices in a Ca^{++} free Ringer medium. If cocaine (0.5 mM) can indeed replace Ca^{++}, or give rise to a diminished ratio K^+/Ca^{++}, the amino acid pattern obtained, as well as the respiratory rate, in a Ca^{++} free medium should change towards the values obtained in a normal Ringer medium.

Results given in Table 29 show that the addition of cocaine (0.5 mM) to a Ca^{++} free medium brings about marked falls in the labelling of glutamic acid, glutamine and γ-aminobutyric acid and in the respiratory rate in the manner anticipated from the neurophysiological results, but the effects of cocaine (0.5 mM) and of Ca^{++} (3.6 mM) are not identical. The fall in respiratory rate is greater than that expected if cocaine is simply replacing Ca^{++} and the labelling of aspartic acid and alanine is not appreciably diminished.

It is concluded, therefore, that cocaine (0.5 mM) exerts a twofold effect, one that is essentially that of replacing Ca^{++} (or diminishing K^+/Ca^{++} by effects on ionic permeability) and another which results in diminished rates of breakdown of pyruvate or oxalacetate so that more of these ketonic acids are available for transamination to alanine and aspartic acid. The latter effect is consistent with the diminished respiratory rate secured by cocaine.

Such observations justify the view that the neurophysiological effects of organic bases may be largely concerned with their interrelations with inorganic cations at special sites on the neuronal surfaces or by their exerting changes of cationic balance at the sites where they are adsorbed. Conceivably they may cause local changes of permeability and hence disturbances of nerve metabolism and function. It has been pointed out recently (483) that certain neuromuscular blocking agents (pyrrolizidine alkaloids, d-tubocurarine) affect mitochondrial permeabilities, the effects being referable to the charges carried on the nitrogen atoms.

BIOCHEMICAL ASPECTS OF SCHIZOPHRENIA

Our survey, brief as it is, has shown that neurological disturbance may be brought about by conditions that affect the energetics of the brain cell, and by substances that interfere with a large variety of the chemical processes necessary for the normal metabolism and functioning of the brain cell. Whilst many disorders of unquestioned organic origin give rise to mental aberrations, and among these may be mentioned the degenerative diseases (including those of demyelination), the diseases of infectious origin such as general paresis and encephalitis, the neoplasms and traumas, the epilepsies and the endocrine and nutritional disorders, the genetically controlled disorders such as lipoidoses and phenylketonuria, the conditions consequent upon the malfunctioning of the various organs of the body such as hepatic coma and bilirubin encephalopathy, most of which have been touched upon in this book, there is the great group of psychoneuroses and psychoses to which so far no mention has been made.

It is now considered that we are entering an important third stage in the development of psychiatry. The first was connected with advances in social reform and descriptive psychiatry, the second with a large body of work on psychodynamics, incorporating the views of Freud and many others who have made such remarkable contributions to our knowledge of the processes of the mind, and the third, which we are now entering, is associated with advances in neurochemistry and pharmacology, an era of psychopharmacology and psychoneurology. This new stage of development must remind us of the often quoted statement, made in 1884, of Thudicum (419), who may be regarded as the founder of modern neurochemistry, "Many forms of insanity are unquestionably the external manifestations of the effects upon the brain substance of poisons fermented within the body, just as mental aberrations accompanying chronic alcoholic intoxication are the accumulated effects of a relatively simple poison fermented out of the body."

No one doubts that the large advances made in psychiatry today are in the field of psychopharmacology (423), and many hypotheses, which stimulate new experimental work and which attempt to correlate the metabolic effects of neurotropic drugs with clinical findings in the psychoses, have been put forward (420). The biochemical theories and concepts relating to mental disorder, and which may be considered in some ways as a development of the older ideas of Kraepelin and Bleuler, have been the subject of a variety of reviews (421), one of the most recent being that of Kety (422).

It has been thought for a long time that schizophrenia has a toxic origin (e.g. 424) and Gjessing (425) has brought forward good evidence for disturbed nitrogen balance in periodic catatonia. The demonstration that amines, normally broken down in the liver, such as tyramine, tryptamine or isoamylamine, interfere with oxidative brain metabolism (280,281) led to a study of processes of detoxication in the liver. It was observed that excretion of hippuric acid after benzoic acid administration is abnormal in catatonic schizophrenia (426). Moreover the conjugation was reported to be abnormal under emotional stress (427) and to be disturbed by administration of the hallucinogenic amine, mescaline (428). Whether, in fact, observations such as these (see also 429) can be considered evidence of the formation of toxic products that affect the brain in schizophrenia, is very debatable, though it is evident that the patients under investigation were definitely exhibiting abnormal metabolic states. However, the facts that certain drugs, such as bulbocapnine and mescaline, which can affect brain metabolism *in vitro* (280), and which are related to normally occurring physiological amines, have very marked effects on brain function, that a drug such as amphetamine, which has value in the treatment of narcolepsy and has central stimulating effects, is an inhibitor of amine oxidase (285), and other observations of like nature have led to a search for the occurrence of abnormal substances, or of normal substances in abnormal amounts, in the tissues of mentally disordered patients. For this purpose, the new sensitive techniques of chromatography have been most helpful and indeed essential.

Although various observations have been made (a) of abnormal quantities of aromatic substances in the urine of schizophrenic patients (430) (b) of the presence of unidentified amines and indoles in such patients (431), it is by no means certain that such substances are invariably present and it is possible that when they are present they have no relation to the mental condition of the patient but to dietary habits or other circumstances (432,422).

The profound effects of a variety of amines (e.g., acetylcholine, serotonin, catecholamines, γ aminobutyric acid) on the functioning of the central nervous system, and the fact that they are produced *in situ*, make it reasonable to suspect that the cerebral dysfunction of psychotic subjects is due to altered biochemical conditions in the brain itself. Presumably, however, the converse might also occur, for the phenomena of neurophysiology and neurobiochemistry represent different facets of the same underlying processes and are dependent on each other. Abnormal quantities of the amines produced elsewhere in the body are unlikely to have large central effects partly because of the obstruction of the blood-brain barrier and partly because of the destructive action of amine oxidases, and other catabolic enzymes, in tissues other than the brain.

Even if it is reasonable to focus attention on the metabolic events proceeding in the brain in cases of mental disorder, we may ask what actual evidence is there that abnormalities in these events are responsible for the manifestations of mental disorder.

The advent of the amine oxidase inhibitors, such as iproniazid (Marsilid), whose effects on the nervous system have been the subject of a recent symposium (433), makes it evident that interference with metabolic events in the brain can be useful in the treatment of mental disorder by producing behavioral changes. For example, Hawkins *et al.* (433) report that iproniazid seems to be more effective in the treatment of psychotic reactions than in the neurotic disorders, the best results being obtained in the psychotic depressive reactions in which a 77% improvement rate is noted. Again, Scanlon (433) and English (433) report that treatment with the amine oxidase inhibitor and that with electrotherapy are complementary, so that the need for the latter is cut by about 90% by combination therapy. English (433) makes the comment "most depressed patients respond to iproniazid, which elevates them, and many manics respond to tranquilising drugs that depress them . . ."

The use of the amine oxidase inhibitors and of the tranquilisers has been responsible for large changes in the treatment of mental disorder and indicates the possibility that the neurochemical events affected by these drugs are involved in the aetiology of the disorder. Nevertheless, it has to be clearly understood that whilst alterations in the levels of substances, such as serotonin and the catecholamines, in the brain are affected by the amine oxidase inhibitors there is no conclusive evidence that these amines are causally involved.

The new techniques that have become available to the biochemist has made it possible to discover a variety of amines in the nervous system, each of which presumably plays its part at some site in the brain. Most knowledge, at present is concerned with serotonin and the catecholamines. It will suffice, here, to point out that levels of serotonin are higher in those parts of the brain associated with emotional activity (434) than elsewhere. Dimethylserotonin (bufotenin) has psychotomimetic properties like those of lysergic acid diethylamide. Reserpine causes a fall in the serotonin level in the brain which reflects to a greater degree the changes in mental effects than the concentration of reserpine itself (435). As already mentioned, administration of 5-hydroxytryptophan increases brain serotonin levels with mental effects somewhat similar to those of lysergic acid diethylamide. The chance discovery of toxic psychoses in tuberculosis patients treated with iproniazid led to the use of this drug for the treatment of depressed states and to the finding that it inhibits amine oxidase, producing increases in the level of serotonin in the brain (436). The level of noradrenaline, like that of serotonin, in the brain falls following reserpine administration. Hoffer (433) considers that anxiety is related to the ratio of adrenaline to indole derivatives in the brain.

The biochemistry and pharmacology of the catecholamines has now grown into a vast subject which has been reviewed recently (437) and there is little doubt that many major advances have yet to be made in this field of enquiry.

Whilst it is important to know that the new drug therapies are most valuable additions to the methods of treatment of mental disorder that have developed in the last thirty or forty years, it would be well to discover if there is any common basis to these therapies that may throw light on the causes of the mental disorders themselves.

When one considers the effects of narcosis treatment and those of insulin and electroshock therapies, it is seen that there is one feature in common, an interference with oxidative events in the brain either by lowered oxygen consumption or by lowered glucose availability. When one turns to therapy with amine oxidase inhibitors or tranquilisers, it is seen that once again interference with certain oxidative events is involved, though in a more specific manner and probably at more specific sites in the nervous system. If all these therapies had a common effect, that of changing the course or speed of oxidative processes in certain structures or centres of the brain which are abnormally active in mental disorder, it would be possible to understand the temporary, and occasionally permanent, alleviation of the disorder. Obviously genetic factors might lead to the development in the nervous system of those areas that do not function normally and which may, therefore, respond in an exceptional manner to environmental stimuli.

BIOCHEMICAL ASPECTS OF MENTAL DEFECT

Mongolism

This condition is characterized by mental defect, maternal age being a highly significant factor in its aetiology. There is also a genetic factor which may make susceptibility in some families greater than others (412,450).

Morphological studies show that mongoloids exhibit degeneration of brain tissue, loss of nerve cells and cortical atrophy. There is, however, no marked difference between the rates of oxygen consumption of mongoloids and of normal subjects, until about the age of 19. After that age, differences between the brain metabolic rates of mongoloids and of normals become marked, as shown by the fact that the cerebral arteriovenous oxygen difference ceases to rise in the mongoloid. Thus, whereas normal AVO_2 is 6.7 volumes per cent in normal adults (over age 19), it is 5.6 volumes per cent in mongoloids between the ages of 20 and 45 (451). Apparently, the development of some components of the cerebral respiratory system is arrested at a relatively early age, a fact consistent with the observation that development of the mongoloid brain ceases at an early age (452).

Endocrine Dystrophies

The endocrine disorders commonly giving rise to mental defect are cretinism and hypothyroidism.

Penrose (450) concludes that cretinism may be the expression of a Mendelian recessive character; when it is recessive, it seems that the heterozygotes (carriers) sometimes show disturbances of thyroid function. Wherever endemic goitre is present, there is also endemic cretinism, the latter usually appearing in the second generation when a normal family moves into a goitrous district. Cretins differ clinically from mongols, showing usually more alertness of mind. There seems to be little doubt that the essential factor in cretinism is a thyroid abnormality. Some forms of cretinism have been traced to specific defects in iodine metabolism e.g. absence of an oxidase converting iodide to iodine (453) and failure to conjugate iodotyrosines (454).

The average cerebral arteriovenous oxygen difference in cretins above the age of 20 is 5.5 volumes per cent, significantly lower than the normal value of 6.7 volumes per cent. There is a lower cerebral metabolic rate which is attributed to an uncompleted development of cerebral enzymes (40). Administration of thyroxin to cretins raises their cerebral metabolic rate by 32% over the controls (40). Hypothyroid subjects often exhibit the listless, and retarded, action accompanying sluggish cerebral metabolic rates; such symptoms usually disappear on thyroid therapy and normal behaviour is obtained.

Other Conditions Exhibiting Mental Defect

Cases of degeneration of basal ganglia (in which there is a strong inheritance factor), many cases (20-50%) of muscular dystrophy, about half the cases of albinism (in which there is an enzymic defect associated with pigment production from dihydroxyphenylalanine) show mental defect.

To this should be added the types of mental defect associated with disorders of lipid metabolism (the lipoidoses), of amino acid metabolism (e.g. phenylketonuria), Wilson's disease (which may more properly be considered a disease implicating copper metabolism), and of carbohydrate metabolism (galactosemia, glycogenosis or von Gierke's disease).

Himwich (40) concludes that there are two types of mental deficiency, one with a normal, and the other with a reduced, cerebral metabolism. Reduced cerebral metabolism occurs in mongolism, cretinism, phenylketonuria, hydrocephalus and microcephalus and possibly amaurotic familial iodiocy. Many undifferentiated mental defectives have normal cerebral metabolic rates.

The importance of genetic factors in cerebral dysfunction is shown by the existence of inborn metabolic errors associated with mental defect. The diseases are comparatively rare and their mode of inheritance is generally autosomal and recessive. It must be remembered, however, that heterozygous carriers of apparently recessive genes causing metabolic defects are relatively common. For example, carriers of phenylketonuria have an incidence of 1% (455) in the general population and may be detected because they have a reduced phenylalanine tolerance (458).

It would appear that many mental defectives, in the undifferentiated group, have normal cerebral metabolic rates, their dysfunction not being attributable to alteration of any specific chemical character; whereas many defectives, classed in groups of diseases often with a strong inheritance factor, owe their mental deficiency to definite biochemical factors whose modes of action are for the most part still unknown.

REFERENCES

1. Gildea, E. F. and Cobb, S.: *Arch. Neurol. & Psychiat. 23:*876, 1930.
2. Lennox, W. G.: *Arch. Neurol. & Psychiat. 36:*375, 1936.
3. Lennox, W. G. and Behnke, A. R.: *Arch. Neurol. & Psychiat. 35:*782, 1936.
4. Bert, P.: *La Pression Barometrique.* Paris, Masson, 1878.
5. Barcroft, J.: *Features in the Architecture of Physiological Function.* Cambridge, Cambridge Univ. Press, 1934.
   Lessons from High Altitudes. Cambridge, Cambridge Univ. Press, 1936.
6. Kety, S. S.: *Metabolism of the Nervous System.* Ed.: Richter, D. New York, Pergamon Press, 1957, p. 221.
7. Hou, C. L.: *J. Orient. Med. 5:*20, 1926.
8. Kety, S. S. and Schmidt, C. F.: *J. Clin. Invest. 27:*476, 1948.
9. Folch-Pi, J.: *Harvard Univ. Monogr. Med. & Pub. Health 9:*17, 1947.
10. Kety, S. S.: *Neurochemistry.* Ed.: Elliott, K. A. C., Page, I. H. and Quastel, J. H. Springfield, Illinois, Charles C Thomas, 1955, p. 294.
11. Heyman, A., Patterson, J. L. and Jones, R. W.: *Circulation. 3:* 558, 1951.
12. Scheinberg, P., Stead, E. A., Brannon, E. S., and Warren, J. V.: *J. Clin. Invest. 29:*1139, 1950.
13. Kety, S. S.: *The Biology of Mental Health and Disease.* Symposium. New York, Paul B. Hoeber, Inc., 1950, p. 20.
14. Gibbs, F. A., Gibbs, E. L. and Lennox, W. G.: *J. Aviation Med. 14:*250, 1943.
15. Schmidt, C. F.: *The Cerebral Circulation in Health and Disease.* Springfield, Ill., Charles C Thomas, 1950.
16. Lassen, N. A.: *Physiol. Rev. 39:*183, 1959.
17. Schmidt, C. F., Kety, S. S. and Pennes, H. H.: *Amer. J. Physiol. 143:* 33, 1945.
18. Hirsch, H., Krenkl, W., Schneider, M. and Schnellenbacher, F.: *Pflug. Arch. ges. Physiol. 26:*402, 1955.
19. Kety, S. S., Polis, B. D., Nadler, C. S., and Schmidt, C. F.: *J. Clin. Invest. 27:*500, 1948.

20. Patterson, J. L., Heyman, A. and Nichols, F. T.: *J. Clin. Invest.* *29:*1327, 1950.
21. Wechsler, R. L., Dripps, R. D. and Kety, S. S.: *Anaesthesiology.* *12:*308, 1951.
22. Himwich, W. A., Hamburger, E., Maresca, R. and Himwich, H. E.: *Amer. J. Psychiat.* *103:* 689, 1947.
23. Battey, L. L., Heyman, A. and Patterson, J. L.: *J.A.M.A.* *152:* 6, 1953.
24. Mangold, R., Sokoloff, L., Conner, E., Kleinerman, J., Therman, P. G. and Kety, S. S.: *J. Clin. Invest.* *34:*1092, 1955.
25. Sokoloff, L., Mangold, R., Wechsler, R. L., Kennedy, C. and Kety, S. S.: *J. Clin. Invest.* *34:*1101, 1955.
26. Kety, S. S., Woodford, R. B., Harmel, M. H., Freyhan, F. A., Appel, K. E. and Schmidt, C. F.: *Amer. J. Psychiat.* *104:*765, 1948.
27. Toman, J. E. P. and Davis, J. P.: *J. Pharmacol.* *97:*425, 1949.
28. Wikler, A.: *Pharmacol. Rev.* *2:*435, 1950.
29. Geiger, A. and Magnes, J.: *Amer. J. Physiol.* *149:*517, 1947.
30. Gibbs, F. A., Maxwell, H. and Gibbs, E. L.: *Arch. Neurol. Psychiat.* *57:*137, 1947.
31. Jasper, H. and Erikson, T. C.: *J. Neurophysiol.* *4:*333, 1941.
32. Gurdjian, E. S., Webster, J. E. and Stone, W. E.: *Proc. A. Res. Nerv. & Ment. Dis.* *26:*184, 1946.
33. Penfield, W., von Santha, K. and Cipriani, A.: *J. Neurophysiol.* *2:* 257, 1939.
34. Schneider, M.: *Metabolism of the Nervous System.* Ed. by Richter, D. New York, Pergamon Press, 1957, p. 238.
35. Heymans, C. and Bouckaert, J. J.: *Compt. rend. Soc. biol.* *119:*324, 1935.
36. McFarland, R. A.: *J. Comp. Psych.* *23:*191; *24:*147, 1937.
37. McFarland, R. A., Knehr, C. H. and Berens, C.: *Am. J. Ophthalmology.* *20:*1204, 1937.
38. Gellhorn, E.: *Ann. Int. Med.* *10:*1267, 1937.
39. McFarland, R. A.: *The Biology of Mental Health and Disease.* Symposium. New York, Paul B. Hoeber, Inc., 1952, p. 335.
40. Himwich, H. E.: *Brain Metabolism and Cerebral Disorders.* Baltimore, Williams and Wilkins, 1951.
41. McIlwain, H.: *Biochemistry and the Central Nervous System.* London, J. and A. Churchill Ltd., 1959.
42. King, B. D., Sokoloff, L. and Wechsler, R. L.: *J. Clin. Invest.* *31:* 273, 1952.
43. Sokoloff, L., Wechsler, R. L., Mangold, R., Balls, K. and Kety, S. S.: *J. Clin. Invest.* *32:*202, 1953.

44. Scheinberg, P.: *J. Clin. Invest. 29:*1010, 1950.
45. Lennox, W. G.: *Arch. Neurol. Psychiat. 36:*375, 1936.
46. Warburg, O., Posener, K., and Negelein, E.: *Biochem. Zeit. 152:* 309, 1924.
47. Jowett, M. and Quastel, J. H.: *Biochem. J. 31:*1101, 1937.
48. Krebs, H. A. and Johnson, W. A.: *Tabulae Biol. 19:*100, 1948.
49. Elliott, K. A. C.: *The Biology of Mental Health and Disease.* Symposium. New York, Paul B. Hoeber, Inc., 1952, p. 54.
50. Dixon, T. F. and Meyer, A.: *Biochem. J. 30:*1577, 1936.
51. Brookens, N. L., Ectors, L. and Gerard, R. W.: *Amer. J. Physiol. 116:*16, 1936.
52. Krebs, H. A. and Rosenhagen, H.: *Zeit. g. Neur. Psych. 134:*643, 1931.
53. Elliott, K. A. C. and Heller, I. H.: *Metabolism of the Nervous System.* Edited by Richter, D. New York, Pergamon Press, 1957, p. 286.
54. Dickens, F. and Greville, G. C.: *Biochem. J. 29:*1468, 1935.
55. Ashford, C. A. and Dixon, K. C.: *Biochem. J. 29:*157, 1935.
56. Buchel, L.: *Anaesthesie Analgesie 10.* No. 1. 1, 1953.
57. Winterstein, H.: *Bethe's Handbuch,* 9, Berlin, Springer, 1929.
58. Bronk, D. W. and Brink, F.: *Fed. Proc. 10:*19, 1951
59. McIlwain, H.: *Biochem. J. 53:*403, 1953.
60. Geiger, A.: *Physiol. Rev. 38:*1, 1958.
61. Loebel, R. O.: *Biochem. Zeit. 161:*219, 1925.
62. Dickens, F. and Simer, F.: *Biochem. J. 25:*985, 1931.
63. Quastel, J. H. and Wheatley, A. H. M.: *Biochem. J. 26:*725, 1932.
64. Gavrilescu, N., Meiklejohn, A. P., Passmore, R. and Peters, R. A.: *Proc. Roy. Soc. London B. 110:*431, 1932.
65. Lindan, O., Quastel, J. H. and Sved, S.: *Canad. J. Biochem. Physiol. 35:*1135, 1145, 1957.
66. Sperry, W. M.: Discussion in *Biochemistry of the Developing Nervous System.* Edited by H. Waelsch. New York, Academic Press, 1955, p. 199.
67. Vignais, P. M., Gallagher, C. H. and Zabin, I.: *J. Neurochem. 2:* 283, 1958.
68. Himwich, H. E. and Fazekas, J. F.: *Endocrinology. 21:*800, 1937.
69. Gibbs, E. L., Lennox, W. G., Nune, L. F. and Gibbs, F. A.: *J. Biol. Chem. 144:*325, 1942.
70. Dixon, K. C.: *Biochem. J. 30:*1479, 1936.
71. Jowett, M. and Quastel, J. H.: *Biochem. J. 31:*565, 1937.
72. Maddock, S., Hawkins, J. E. and Holmes, E.: *Amer. J. Physiol. 125:*551, 1939.
73. McIlwain, H.: *J. Neurol. Neurosurg. Psychiat. 16:* 257, 1953: *Biochem. J. 55:*618, 1953.

74. Kratzing, C. C.: *Biochem. J. 54:*312, 1953.
75. Ghosh, J. J. and Quastel, J. H.: *Nature. 174:*28, 1954.
76. Fenn, W. O. and Gerschman, R. J.: *Gen. Physiol. 33:*195, 1950.
77. Hodgkin, A. L.: *Biol. Rev. 26:*339, 1951.
    Hodgin, A. L. and Huxley, A. F.: *Cold Spring Harbor Symp. 17:* 43, 1952.
78. Shanes, A. M.: *Electrolytes in Biological Systems.* Symposium. Washington, American Physiol. Soc., 1955.
79. Bishop, G. H.: *J. Cell. Comp. Physiol. 1:*177, 1932.
80. Schmitt, F. O. and Schmitt, O. H.: *Amer. J. Physiol. 97:*302, 1931.
81. Keynes, R. D.: *Biochemistry of the Central Nervous System.* Symposium. Proc. 4th International Congress of Biochem. Vienna. Edited by F. Brucke. New York, Pergamon Press, 1959, p. 18.
82. Dawson, R. M. C. and Richter, D.: *Amer. J. Physiol. 160:*203, 1950.
83. Shapot, V. S.: *Metabolism of the Nervous System.* Symposium. Edited by Richter, D. New York, Pergamon Press, 1957, p. 257.
84. Quastel, J. H. and Wooldridge, W. R.: *Biochem. J. 22:*689, 1928.
85. Kimura, Y. and Niwa, T.: *Nature. 171:*881, 1953.
    Tsukada, Y. and Takaguchi, O.: *Nature. 175:*725, 1955.
86. Takagaki, G., Hirano, S. and Tsukada, Y.: *J. Biochem. Japan. 45:* 41, 1958.
87. Parmar, S. and Quastel, J. H.: In Quastel, J. H. *Biochemistry of the Central Nervous System.* Symposium. Edited by Brucke, F. Proc. 4th Inter. Congress Biochem. Vienna. New York, Pergamon Press, 1959, p. 40.
88. Kini, M. M. and Quastel, J. H.: *Nature. 184:*252, 1959.
89. Mann, P. J. G., Tennenbaum, M. and Quastel, J. H.: *Biochem. J. 33:*822, 1939.
90. Rowsell, E. V.: *Biochem. J. 57:*666, 1954.
91. McIlwain, H.: *Physiol. Rev. 36:*355, 1956.
92. Olsen, N. S. and Klein, J. R.: *Res. Publ. Ass. Nerv. Ment. Dis. 26:* 118, 1946.
93. Stone, W. E., Webster, J. E. and Gurdjian, E. S.: *J. Neurophysiol. 8:*233, 1945.
94. Vernon, H. M.: *J. Physiol. 42:*402, 1911; *43:*96, 1911.
95. Quastel, J. H. and Wheatley, A. H. M.: *Proc. Roy. Soc. (Lond.) B. 112:*60, 1933.
96. Elliott, K. A. C.: *Neurochemistry.* Edited by Elliott, K. A. C., Page, I. H. and Quastel, J. H. Springfield, Ill., Charles C Thomas, 1955, p. 53.
97. Potter, V., Schneider, W. C. and Liebl, G. J.: *Cancer Res. 5:*21, 1945.
98. Tyler, D. B. and van Harreveld, A.: *Amer. J. Physiol. 136:*500, 1942.

99. Himwich, H. E. and Fazekas, J. F.: *Amer. J. Physiol. 132:*454, 1941.

100. Flexner, L. B. and Flexner, J. B.: *Anat. Rec. 91:*274, 1945.

101. Himwich, H. E., Fazekas, J. F., Herrlich, H. C. and Rich, E.: *Amer. J. Physiol. 137:*327, 1942.

102. Tyler, D. B.: *Proc. Soc. Exp. Biol. Med. 49:*537, 1942.

103. Nachmansohn, D.: *J. Neurophysiol. 3:*396, 1940.
    Youngstrom, K. A.: *J. Neurophysiol. 4:*473, 1941.

104. Ashby, W. and Butler, E.: *J. Biol. Chem. 175:*425, 1948.
    Ashby, W. and Schuster, E. M.: *J. Biol. Chem. 184:*109, 1950.

105. Sperry, W. M.: *Neurochemistry.* Edited by Elliott, K. A. C., Page, I. H. and Quastel, J. H. Springfield, Ill., Charles C Thomas, 1955, p. 234.

106. Kety, S. S.: *Biochemistry of the Developing Nervous System.* Symposium. Edited by Waelsch, H. New York, Academic Press, 1955, p. 208.

107. Kennedy, C., Sokoloff, L. and Anderson, W.: *Am. J. Diseases Children,* (*see* 106).

108. Kennedy, C.: Quoted by Kety, S. S. (106).

109. Pope, A., Hess, H. H. and Allen, J. N.: *Progr. in Neurobiology. 2:* 182, 1957.

110. Shenkin, H. A., Novak, P., Goluboff, B., Soffe, A. M. and Bortin, L.: *J. Clin, Invest. 32:*459, 1953.

111. Scheinberg, P., Blackburn, I., Rich, M. and Saslow, M.: *Arch. Neurol. Psychiat. 70:*77, 1953.

112. Fazekas, J. F., Alman, R. W. and Bessman, A. N.: *Am. J. Med. Sc. 223:*245, 1952.

113. Fazekas, J. F., Kleh, J. and Witkin, L.: *J. Am. Geriatrics Soc. 1:* 836, 1953.

114. Richter, D.: *Biochemistry of the Developing Nervous System.* Symposium. Edited by Waelsch, H. New York, Academic Press, 1955, p. 225.

115. McIlwain, H.: *Brit. J. Pharmacol. 6:*531, 1951.

116. Mann, F. C.: *Medicine. 6:*419, 1927.

117. Loman, J.: *Arch. Neurol. Psychiat* (Chicago). *45:*282, 1941.

118. Hoagland, H., Rubin, M. A. and Cameron, D. E.: *Am. J. Physiol. 120:*559, 1937.

119. Weil-Malherbe, H.: *J. Mental Sc. 98:*565, 1952.

120. Mayer-Gross, W. and Walker, J. W.: *Biochem. J. 44:*92, 1949.

121. Mann, F. C. and Magath, T. B.: *Arch. Int. Med. 30:*171, 1922.

122. Geiger, K., Magnes, J., Taylor, R. M. and Veralli, M.: *Amer. J. Physiol. 177:*138, 1954.

123. Quastel, J. H.: *Am. J. Clin. Nutrition 8:*137 1960.

124. Tschirgi, R. D., Gerard, R. W., Jenerick, H., Boyarsky, L. L. and Hearon, J. Z.: *Fed. Proc. 8:*166, 1949.

125. Larrabee, M. G., Edwards, C. and Ramos, J. G.: *Fed. Proc. 10:* 79, 1951.
126. Libet, B. and Gerard, R. W.: *J. Neurophysiol. 2:*153, 1939.
127. Geiger, A., Magnes, J. and Geiger, R. S.: *Nature. 170:*754, 1952.
128. Abood, L. G. and Geiger, A.: *Am. J. Physiol. 182:*557, 1955.
129. Dickens, F. and Greville, G. D.: *Biochem. J. 27:*1134, 1933.
130. Quastel, J. H. and Wheatley, A. H. M.: *J. Biol. Chem. 199,* LXXX-LXXXI, 1937.
131. Elliott, K. A. C. and Rosenfeld M., *Canad. J. Biochem. Physiol. 36:*721, 1958.
132. Folch, J.: In *Psychiatric Research.,* ch. 2. Monographs in Med. and Pub. Health. No. 9. Cambridge, Massachusetts, Harvard University Press.
133. Folch, J., Lees, M. and Sloane-Stanley, G. H.: *Metabolism of the Nervous System.* Symposium. Edited by Richter, D. New York, Pergamon Press, 1957, p. 174.
134. Brink, F.: *Metabolism of the Nervous System.* Symposium. Edited by Richter, D. New York, Pergamon Press, 1957, p. 187.
135. Larrabee, M. G., Horowicz, P., Stekiel, W. and Dolivo, M.: *Metabolism of the Nervous System.* Symposium. Edited by Richter, D. New York, Pergamon Press, 1957, p. 208.
136. Dixon, K. C.: *Biochem. J. 44:*187, 1949.
137. Stern, J. R., Eggleston, L. V., Hems, R., and Krebs, H. A.: *Biochem. J. 44:*410, 1949.
138. Krebs, H. A. and Kornberg, H. L.: *Energy Transformations in Living Matter.* Berlin, Springer, 1957.
139. Ball, E. G.: *Ann. N. Y. Acad. Sc. 45:*363, 1944.
140. Martius, C.: *Biochem. Zeit. 326:*26, 1954; *327:*1, 1955.
141. Braunstein, A. E.: *Adv. Protein Chem. 3:*1, 1947.
142. Braunstein, A. E.: *Proc. Intern. Symp. Enz. Chem. Tokyo.* Tokyo, Maruzen, 1958, p. 135.
143. Gunsalus, I. C.: *The Mechanism of Enzyme Action.* Edited by McElroy, W. D. and Glass, B. Baltimore, Johns Hopkins Press, 1954, p. 545. *Fed. Proc. 13:*715, 1954.
144. Lehninger, A. L.: *Phosphorus Metabolism.* Edited by McElroy, W. D. and Glass, B. Baltimore, Johns Hopkins Press, 1951, I, 344. *Oxidative phosphorylation, Harvey Lect. 49:*176, 1955.
145. Lardy, H. A. and Wellman, H.: *J. Biol. Chem. 195:*215, 1952.
146. Chance, B.: *Harvey Lect. 49:*145, 1955.
147. Rabinowitz, M., Stulberg, M. P. and Boyer, P. D.: *Science. 114:* 641, 1951.

148. Krebs, H. A.: The tricarboxylic acid cycle, In Greenberg, D. M.: *Chemical Pathways of Metabolism I.* New York, Academic Press, 1954, p. 109.

149. Warburg, O. and Christian, W.: *Biochem. Zeit. 287:*440, 1936. Warburg, O., Christian, W. and Griese, A.: *Biochem. Z. 282:* 157, 1935.

150. Glock, G. E. and McLean, P.: *Biochem. J. 55:*400, 1953.

151. Dickens, F. and Glock, G. E.: *Biochem. J. 50:*81, 1951.

152. Racker, E., de la Haba, G. L. and Leder, I. G.: *J. Am. Chem. Soc. 75:*1010, 1953; *J. Biol. Chem. 214:*409, 1955.

153. Jowett, M. and Quastel, J. H.: *Biochem. J. 31:*275, 1937.

154. Baker, Z., Fazekas, J. F. and Himwich, H. E.: *J. Biol. Chem. 125:* 545, 1938.

155. Hunter, F. E.: *Phosphorus Metabolism. Vol. I.* Edited by McElroy, W. D. and Glass, B. Baltimore, Johns Hopkins Press, 1951.

156. Ashby, W. M.: *Biology of Mental Health and Disease.* Discussion. New York, Hoeber, 1952, p. 467.

157. Lardy, H. A. and Ziegler, J. A.: *J. Biol. Chem. 159:*343, 1945.

158. Coxon, R. V.: *Metabolism of the Nervous System.* Symposium. Edited by Richter, D. New York, Pergamon Press, 1957, p. 303.

159. Lehmann, H.: *Biology of Mental Health and Disease.* Symposium. New York, P. B. Hoeber, Inc., 1952, p. 582. Zimmerman, H. M.: *Proc. A. Res. Nerv. Ment. Dis. 22:*49, 1943.

160. Spies, T. D., Aring, C. D., Gelperin, J. and Bean, W. B.: *Am. J. Med. Sc. 196:*461, 1938.

161. Mann, P. J. G. and Quastel, J. H.: *Biochem. J. 35:*502, 1941.

162. Kaplan, N. O.: *Consciousness and the Chemical Environment of the Brain.* Report of the 25th Ross Research Conference. 1958.

163. Dagg, C. P. and Karnofsky, D. A.: *Fed. Proc. 17:*361, 1958.

164. Yudkin, J.: *Physiol. Rev. 29:*389, 1949; *Biochem. J. 48:*608, 1951. Salem, H. M.: *Biochem. J. 57:*227, 1954.

165. Ochoa, S. and Peters, R. A.: *Biochem. J. 32:*1501, 1938; *Nature. 142:*356, 1938.

166. Wooley, D. W. and White, A. G. C.: *J. Biol. Chem. 149:*285, 1943.

167. Thompson, R. H. S. and Cumings, J. N.: *Biochemical Disorders in Human Diseases.* London, Churchill, 1957.

168. Street, H. R., Cowgill, G. R. and Zimmerman, H. M.: *J. Nutrition. 22:* 7, 1941.

169. Adams, D. H. and |Quastel, J. H.: *Proc. Roy. Soc. London, B. 145.* 472, 1956.

170. Quastel, J. H. and Wheatley, A. H. M.: *Biochem. J. 25:*629, 1931.

171. Brierley, J. B.: *Metabolism of the Nervous System*. Symposium. Edited by Richter, D. New York, Pergamon Press, 1957, p. 121.
172. Krogh, A.: *Proc. Roy. Soc. London, B. 133:*140, 1946.
173. Bakay, L.: *The Blood-Brain Barrier*. Springfield, Illinois, Charles C Thomas, 1956.
174. Hahn, L. and Hevesy, G.: *Acta physiol. scandinav. 1:*347, 1940.
175. Manery, F. F.: *Biology of Mental Health and Disease*. Symposium. New York, P. Hoeber, Inc., 1952, p. 124.
176. Terner, C., Eggleston, L. V. and Krebs, H. A.: *Biochem. J. 47:* 139, 1950.
    Krebs, H. A., Eggleston, L. V. and Terner, C.: *Biochem. J. 48:* 530, 1951.
177. Davies, R. E. and Krebs, H. A.: *Biochem. Soc. Sympos. 8:*77, 1952.
178. Noonan, T. R., Fenn, W. O. and Haege, L.: *Am. J. Physiol. 132:* 474, 1941.
    Ginsburg, J. M. and Wilde, W. S.: *Am. J. Physiol. 179:*63, 1954.
179. Waelsch, H.: *Biochemistry of the Developing Nervous System*. Symposium. New York, Academic Press, 1955, p. 187.
180. Himwich, W. H., Peterson, J. C. and Allen, M. L.: *Neurology. 7:* 705, 1957.
181. Waelsch, H.: *Symposium on Neurochemistry of Nucleotides and Amino Acids*. Edited by Brady, R. O. and Tower, D. B. Amer. Acad. Neurology.
182. Heinz, E. and Walsh, P. M.: *J. Biol. Chem. 233:*1488, 1958.
    Heinz, E.: *J. Biol. Chem. 211:*781, 1954.
183. Friedberg, F., Tarver, H. and Greenberg, D. M.: *J. Biol. Chem. 173:*355, 1948.
184. Gaitonde, M. K. and Richter, D.: *Metabolism of the Nervous System*. Symposium. Edited by Richter, D. New York, Pergamon Press, 1957, 449.
185. Takagaki, G., Hirano, S. and Nagata, Y.: *J. Neurochem. 4:*124, 1959.
186. Lajtha, A., Furst, S., Gerstein, A. and Waelsch, H.: *J. Neurochem. 1:*289, 1957.
187. Klein, J. R., Hurwitz, R. and Olsen, N. S.: *J. Biol. Chem. 164:* 509, 1946.
188. Vladimirov, G. E.: *Biochemistry of the Developing Nervous System*. Edited by Waelsch, H. New York, Academic Press, 1955, p. 218.
189. Stern, W. E. and Marshall, C.: *Proc. Soc. Exper. Biol. & Med. 78:* 16, 1951.
190. Moore, G. E.: *Science. 107:*569, 1948.
191. Bakay, L.: *Metabolism of the Nervous System*. Edited by Richter, D. New York, Pergamon Press, 1957, p. 136.

192. Hawking, F., Hennelly, T. J. and Quastel, J. H.: *J. Pharmacol.-Exp. Therap. 59:*157, 1937.
Gordon, J. J. and Quastel, J. H.: *Biochem. J. 42:*337, 1948.
*Nature. 159:*97, 1947.

193. Goodman, L. and Gilman, A.: *The Pharmacological Basis of Therapeutics.* New York, MacMillan, 1941.

194. Harris, T. A. B.: *The Mode of Action of Anaesthetics.* Edinburgh, Livingstone, 1951.

195. Holmes, J. H. and Tower, D. B.: *Neurochemistry.* Edited by Elliott, K. A. C., Page, I. H. and Quastel, J. H. Springfield, Illinois, Charles C Thomas, 1955, p. 262.

196. White, J. C., Verlot, M., Selverstone, B. and Beecher, H. K.: *Arch. Surg. 44:*1, 1942.

197. Elliott, K. A. C. and Jasper, H. H.: *J. Neurosurg. 6:*140, 1949.

198. Cannon, W. B.: *Am. J. Physiol. 6:*91, 1901.

199. Elliott, K. A. C.: *Proc. Soc. Exper. Biol. & Med. 63:*234, 1946.

200. Quastel, J. H. and Scholefield, P. G.: *Am. J. Med. 25:*420, 1958.

201. Magee, P. N., Stoner, H. B. and Barnes, J. M.: *J. Path. Bact. 73:*107, 1957.

202. Stoner, H. B., Barnes, J. M. and Duff, J. I.: *Brit. J. Pharm. 10:*16, 1955.

203. Aldridge, W. N. and Cremer, J. E.: *Biochem. J. 61:*406, 1955.

204. Cremer, J. E.: *Biochem. J. 67:*87, 1957.

205. Kehoe, R. A. and Thamann, F.: *Am. J. Hyg. 13:*478, 1931.
Branch, F.: *Zeit. Klin. Med. 143:*378, 1943.
Morelli, A. and Preziosi, P.: *Boll. Soc. Ital. Biol. Sper. 29:*1453, 1953.

206. Vardanis, A. and Quastel, J. H., in Quastel, J. H.: *Biochemistry of the Central Nervous System.* Symposium. Proc. 4th Inter. Congress Biochem. Vienna. Edited by Brucke, F. New York, Pergamon Press, 1959, p. 90.

207. MacIntosh, F. C., Birks, R. I. and Sastry, P. B.: *Nature. 178:*1181, 1956.
Gardiner, J. E.: *J. Physiol. 138:*13, 1957.

208. Prados y Such, M.: *Arch. Psychiat. 105:*17, 1936.
Bjerner, B., Broman, T. and Swennson, A.: *Acta Psychiat. Neurol. 19:*431, 1944.

209. Yannet, H.: *Arch. Neurol. Psychiat. 42:*237, 1939.
Colfer, H. F.: *A. Res. Nerv. & Ment. Dis. Proc. 26:*98, 1947.

210. Himwich, H. E.: *Biology of Mental Health and Disease.* Symposium. New York, P. B. Hoeber, Inc., 1952, p. 548.

211. Kamin, H. and Handler, P.: *J. Biol. Chem. 188:*193, 1951.
212. Waelsch, H.: *Metabolism of the Nervous System.* Edited by Richter, D. New York, Pergamon Press, 1957, p. 431.
213. Waelsch, H.: *Lancet. 257:*1, 1949.
214. Sky-Peck, H. H., Pearson, H. E. and Visser, D. W.: *J. Biol. Chem. 223:*1033, 1956.
215. Beloff-Chain, A., Catanzaro, R., Chain, E. B., Masi, I. and Pocchiari, F.: *Proc. Roy. Soc. London, B. 144:*22, 1955.
216. Berl, S. and Waelsch, H.: *J. Neurochem. 3:*161, 1958.
217. Sporn, M. B., Dingman, W. and Defalco, A.: *J. Neurochem. 4:*141, 1959.
     Dingman, W. and Sporn, M. B.: *J. Neurochem. 4:*148, 1959.
218. Krebs, H. A.: *Biochem. J. 29:*1951, 1935.
219. Weil-Malherbe, H.: *Biochem. J. 32:*2257, 1938.
220. Braganca, B. M., Quastel, J. H. and Schucher, R.: *Arch. Biochem. Biophys. 41:*478, 1952.
221. Weil-Malherbe, H.: *Biochem. J. 30:*665, 1936.
222. Von Euler, H., Adler, E., Gunther, G. and Das, N. B.: *Ztschr. Physiol. Chem. 254:61,* 1938.
223. Tower, D. B.: *Biochemistry of the Central Nervous System.* Proc. 4t Inter. Cong. Biochem. Vienna. Edited by Brucke, F. New York, Pergamon Press, 1959, p. 213.
224. Bessman, S. P., Rossen, J. and Laine, E. C.: *J. Biol. Chem. 201:* 385, 1953.
225. Roberts, E.: *Progr. Neurobiol. 1:*11, 1956.
226. Tsukada, Y., Nagata, Y. and Takagaki, G.: *Proc. Japan Acad. 33:* 510, 1957.
227. Sugiura, M.: *Jap. J. Pharmacol. 7:6,* 1957.
228. Pisano, J. J., Mitoma, C. and Udenfriend, S.: *Nature. 180:*1125, 1957.
229. Schneckloth, R. E., Page, I. H. and Corcoran, A. C.; *Circulation. 19:*766, 1959.
230. Udenfriend, S.: *Biochemistry of the Central Nervous System.* Proc. 4th Inter. Cong. Biochem. Vienna. Edited by Brücke, F. New York, Pergamon Press, 1959, p. 301.
231. Albers, R. W. and Salvador, R. A.: *Science. 128:*359, 1958.
232. Roberts, E., Frankel, S. and Harman, P. J.: *Proc. Soc. Exp. Biol. & Med. 74:*383, 1950.
     Roberts, E. and Frankel, S.: *J. Biol. Chem. 187:*55, 1950.
     Awapara, J., Landua, A. J., Fuerst, R. and Seale, B.: *J. Biol. Chem. 187:*35, 1950.
233. Florey, E.: *Naturwissenschaften. 40:*413, 1953.

234. Bazemore, A. W., Elliott, K. A. C. and Florey, E.: *Nature. 178:* 1052, 1956.
235. Hayashi, T. and Nagai, K.: *Abst. Commun. XX. Int. Physiol. Cong.* p. 410, 1956.
236. Elliott, K. A. C., Roberts, E. and Baxter, C. F.; *Biochemistry of the Central Nervous System.* Proc. 4th Inter. Cong. Biochem. Vienna. Edited by Brucke, F. New York, Pergamon Press, 1959, pp. 251, 268.
237. Costa, A. and Himwich, H. E.: *(ibid)*, p. 283.
238. Von Euler, U. S.: *Neurochemistry.* Edited by Elliott, K. A. C., Page, I. H. and Quastel, J. H. Springfield, Illinois, Charles C. Thomas, 1955, p. 426.
239. Blaschko, H.: *J. Physiol. 101:*337, 1942.
240. Holtz, P., Heise, R. and Ludtke, K.: *Arch. f. exper. path. u pharmakol. 191:*87, 1938-39.
241. Vogt, M.: *J. Physiol. 123:*451, 1954.
242. Braunstein, A. E.: *Proc. Intern. Symp. Enz. Chem.* Tokyo, Maruzen, 1958, p. 135.
243. Braunstein, A. E.: *Advances in Protein Chem. 3:*1, 1947.
244. Hoare, D. S. and Snell, E. E.: *Proc. Intern. Symp. Enz. Chem.* Tokyo, Maruzen, 1958, p. 142.
245. Snell, E. E.: *J. Biol. Chem. 154:*313, 1945; *J. Amer. Chem. Soc. 67:* 194, 1945.
   Snell, E. E. and Rannefeld, A. N.: *J. Biol. Chem. 157:*475, 1945.
246. Maloney, C. J. and Parmelee, A. H.: *J. A. Med. Soc. 154:*405, 1954.
   Hunt, A. D., Stokes, J., McCorry, W. W. and Stroud, H. H.: *Pediatrics. 13:*140, 1954.
247. Roberts, E., Younger, F. and Frankel, S.: *J. Biol. Chem. 191:*277, 1951.
248. Killam, K. F. and Bain, J. A.: *J. Pharmacol. Exp-Therap. 119:*255, 263, 1957.
249. Page, I. H.: *Physiol. Rev. 38:*277, 1958.
250. Bessman, S. P., Merlis, J. K. and Borges, F.: *Proc. Soc. Exper. Biol. & Med. 95:*502, 1957.
251. Brodie, B. B. and Shore, P. A.: *Ann. N. Y. Acad. Sc. 66:*631, 1957.
252. Freter, K., Weissbach, H., Redfield, B. G., Udenfriend, S. and Witkop, B.: *J. Amer. Chem. Soc. 80:*983, 1958.
253. Krebs, H. A.: *Biochem. J. 29:*1151, 1935.
254. Speck, J. F.: *J. Biol. Chem. 179:*1405, 1949.
   Elliott, W. H.: *Biochem. J. 49:*1, 1951.
255. Weil-Malherbe, H.: *Biochemistry of the Developing Nervous System.* New York, Academic Press, 1955, p. 458.

256. Lajtha, A., Mela, P. and Waelsch, H.: *J. Biol. Chem. 205:*553, 1953.
257. Meister, A. and Tice, S. V.: *J. Biol. Chem. 187:*173, 1950.
258. Guha, S. R. and Ghosh, J. J.: *Ann. Biochem. & Exper. Med.* (Calcutta) *19:*33, 1959.
259. DuRuisseau, J. P., Greenstein, J. P., Winitz, M. and Birnbaum, S. M.: *Arch. Biochem. Biophys. 68:*161, 1957.
260. Flock, E. V., Block, M. A., Grindlay, J. H., Mann, F. C. and Bollman, J. L.: *J. Biol. Chem. 200:*529, 1953.
261. Richter, D. and Dawson, R. M. C.: *J. Biol. Chem. 176:*1199, 1948.
262. Vrba, R.: *Nature. 176:*117, 1258, 1955; *J. Neurochem. 1:*12, 1956.
263. Guha, S. R. and Ghosh, J. J.: *Ann. Biochem. & Exper. Med.* (Calcutta) *19:*67, 1959.
264. Price, J. L., Waelsch, H. and Putnam, J. J.: *J. A. M. A. 122:* 1153, 1943.
265. Davenport, V. D. and Davenport, H. W.: *J. Nutrition. 36:*263, 1948.
266. Albert, K., Hoch, P. and Waelsch, H.: *J. Nerv. & Ment. Dis. 104:* 263, 1946.
267. Strecker, H. J.: *Metabolism of the Nervous System.* Edited by Richter, D. New York, Pergamon Press, 1957, p. 459.
268. Weil-Malherbe, H.: *J. Ment. Sc. 95:*930, 1949; *98:*565, 1952.
269. Mellanby, E.: *Brit. M. J. 2:*885, 1946.
    Moran, T.: *Lancet. 2:*289, 1947.
270. Braganca, B. M., Faulkner, P. and Quastel, J. H.: *Biochem. Biophys. Acta. 10:*83, 1953.
271. Rabinovitz, M., Olson, M. E. and Greenberg, D. M.: *J. Biol. Chem. 222:*879, 1956. *Cancer Research. 19:*388, 1959.
272. Heald, P. J.: *Biochem. J. 66:*659, 1957; Abstr. 4th Inter. Cong. Biochem. Vienna, 1958, p. 75.
273. Porter, H. and Folch, J.: *J. Neurochem. 1:*260, 1957.
274. Gaitonde, M. K. and Richter, D.: *Proc. Roy. Soc. London, B. 145:* 83, 1956.
275. Lajtha, A., Furst, S. and Waelsch, H.: *J. Neurochem. 1:*289, 1957.
276. Hyden, H.: *Nature. 184:*433, 1959.
277. Quastel, J. H. and Bickis, I. J.: *Nature. 183:*281, 1959.
278. Block, W.: *Hoppe-Seyler Ztschr. 296:*108, 1954.
279. Clarke, D. D., Neidle, A., Sarkar, N. K. and Waelsch, H.: *Arch. Biochem. Biophys. 71:*277, 1957.
280. Quastel, J. H. and Wheatley, A. H. M.: *Biochem. J. 27:*1609, 1933.
281. Pugh, C. E. M. and Quastel, J. H. *Biochem. J. 31:*286, 1937; *31:*2306, 1937.
282. Blaschko, H., Richter, D. and Schlossman, H.: *Biochem. J. 31:* 2187, 1937.

283. Loeper, M.: *Presse Med.* *45:*1603, 1937.
284. Nieuwenhuyzen, F. J.: *Proc. Acad. Sc. Amsterdam. 39:*1153, 1936; *41:*316, 1938.
285. Mann, P. J. G. and Quastel, J. H.: *Nature. 144:*943, 1939; *Biochem. J. 34:*414, 1940.
286. De Jong, H.: *Ztschr. ges. Neurol. Psychiat. 139:*468, 1932.
    Alles, G. A.: *Neuropharmacology.* Trans. 4th Macy Foundation Conference. Edited by Abrahamson, H. A. New York, Macy, 1959, p. 181.
287. Rapport, M. M., Green, A. A. and Page, I. H.: *Science. 108:*329, 1948.
288. Udenfriend, S., Bogdanski, D. F. and Weissbach, H.: *Metabolism of the Nervous System.* Edited by Richter, D. New York, Pergamon Press, 1957, p. 566.
289. Zeller, E. A., Barsky, J. and Berman, E. R.: *J. Biol. Chem. 214:* 267, 1955.
290. Gaddum, J. H.: *Ciba Foundation Symp. on Hypertension.* Boston, Little, Brown & Co., 1954, p. 75.
    Wooley, D. W. and Shaw, E.: *Proc. Nat. Acad. Sc. 40:*228, 1954; *J. Pharmacol. 121:*13, 1957.
291. Shore, D. A., Silver, S. L. and Brodie, B. B.: *Science. 122:*284, 1955.
292. Shore, P. A., Mead, J. A. R., Kuntzman, R. G., Spector, S. and Brodie, B. B.: *Science. 126:*1063, 1957.
293. Vogt, M.: *Biochemistry of the Central Nervous System.* Proc. 4th Intern. Cong. Biochem. Vienna. Edited by Brucke, F. New York, Pergamon Press, 1959, p. 279.
294. Von Euler, U. S.: *Neurochemistry.* Edited by Elliott, K. A. C., Page, I. H. and Quastel, J. H. Springfield, Illinois, Charles C Thomas, 1955, p. 426.
    Metabolism of the Nervous System. Edited by Richter, D. New York, Pergamon Press, 1957, p. 543.
295. Wilson, S. A. K.: *Neurology.* London, Arnold, 1947.
296. Cumings, J. N.: *Brain. 71:*410, 1948; *74:*10, 1951.
297. Scheinberg, I. H.: *Progr. Neurobiol. 1:*52, 1956.
298. Folling, A.: *Hoppe-Seyler Ztschr. 227:*169, 1934.
299. Jervis, G. A.: *J. Biol. Chem. 169:*651, 1947.
300. Knox, W. E. and Hsia, D. Y.: *Amer. J. Med. 22:*687, 1957.
    Hsia, D. Y., Knox, W. E., Quinn, K. V. and Paine, R. S.: *Pediatrics. 21:*178, 1958.
301. Bickel, H.: *Exper. Med. and Surg. 12:*114, 1954.
    Armstrong, M. D. and Tyler, F. H.: *J. Clin. Invest. 34:*565, 1955.
302. Penrose, L. and Quastel, J. H.: *Biochem. J.: 31:*266, 1937.

303. Boscott, R. J. and Bickel, H.: *Biochem. J. 56:*i, 1954.
    Bickel, H., Boscott, R. J. and Gerrard, J.: *Biochemistry of the Developing Nervous System.* Edited by Waelsch, H. New York, Academic Press, Inc., 1955, p. 417.
304. Bickis, I. J., Kennedy, J. P. and Quastel, J. H.: *Nature. 179:*1124, 1957.
305. Welsh, J. H. quoted in Udenfriend *et al.* (288).
306. Symposium: Amine oxidase inhibitors. *Ann. N. Y. Acad. Sc. 80:* 551, 1959.
307. La Brosse, E. H., Axelrod, J. and Kety, S. S.: *Science. 128:*593, 1958.
    Axelrod, J. and Larothe, N. J.: *Science. 130:*800, 1959.
308. Weil-Malherbe, H.: *Biochemistry of the Central Nervous System.* Proc. 4th Inter. Cong. Biochem. Vienna. Edited by Brucke, F. New York, Pergamon Press, 1959, p. 190.
309. Werle, E. and Palm, D.: *Biochem. Ztschr. 323:*255, 1952.
310. Wert, G. B.: *Metabolism of the Nervous System.* Edited by Richter, D. New York, Pergamon Press, 1957, p. 578.
311. Burgen, A. S. V. and MacIntosh, F. C.: *Neurochemistry.* Edited by Elliott, K. A. C., Page, I. H. and Quastel, J. H. Springfield, Illinois, Charles C Thomas, 1955, p. 311.
312. Hebb, C. O.: *Physiol. Rev. 37:*196, 1957.
313. Eccles, J. C.: *Neurophysiological Basis of Mind.* Oxford, Clarendon Press, 1953.
314. Feldberg, W.: *Metabolism of the Nervous System.* Edited by Richter, D. New York, Pergamon Press, 1957, p. 493.
315. Dale, H. H.: *J. Physiol. 48:*3, 1914.
316. Dale, H. H., Feldberg, W. and Vogt, M.: *J. Physiol. 86:*353, 1936.
    Brown, G. L., Dale, H. H. and Feldberg, W.: *J. Physiol. 87:* 394, 1936.
    Dale, H. H.: *Proc. Roy. Soc. Med. 28:*319, 1935.
    Brown, G. L.: *J. Physiol. 89:*438, 1937.
317. Eccles, J. C. and O'Connor, W. J.: *J. Physiol. 97:*44, 1939.
    Goepfert, H. and Schaeffer, H.: *Pflugers Arch. ges. Physiol. 239:* 597, 1937.
318. Nachmansohn, D.: *Chemical and Molecular Basis of Nerve Activity.* New York, Academic Press, 1959.
319. Quastel, J. H., Tennenbaum, M. and Wheatley, A. H. M.: *Biochem. J. 30:*1668, 1936.
320. Stedman, E. and Stedman, E.: *Nature. 141:*39, 1938.
321. Mann, P. J. G., Tennenbaum, M. and Quastel, J. H.: *Biochem. J. 32:*243, 1938.

322. Braganca, B. M. and Quastel, J. H.: *Nature. 169:*695, 1952.
323. Whittaker, V. P.: *Biochem. J. 68:*21P.
324. MacIntosh, F. C.: *J. Physiol. 93:*46, 1938.
    Kahlson, G. and MacIntosh, F. C.: *J. Physiol. 96:*277, 1938.
325. Nachmansohn, D. and Machado, A. L.: *J. Neurophysiol. 6:*397, 1943.
326. Koelle, G. B.: *J. Pharmacol. & Exper-Therap. 114:*167, 1955.
327. Rowsell, S. V.: *Biochem. J. 57:*666, 1954.
328. Feldberg, W. and Vogt, M.: *J. Physiol. 107:*372, 1948.
329. Hebb, C. O. and Silver, A.: *J. Physiol. 134:*718, 1956.
330. Burgen, A. S. V. and Chipman, L. M.: *J. Physiol. 114:* 296, 1951.
331. Richter, D. and Crossland, J.: *Am. J. Physiol. 114:*247, 1949.
332. Mann, P. J. G. and Quastel, J. H.: *Nature. 145:*856, 1940.
333. Harpur, R. P. and Quastel, J. H.: *Nature. 164:*779, 1949.
334. MacIntosh, F. C. and Oborin, P. E.: *Abstr. 19th Int. Physiol. Cong.* 380, 1953.
335. Wilson, I. B.: *J. Biol. Chem. 190:*111, 1951; *199:*113, 1952.
336. Greig, M. E. and Mayberry, T. C.: *J. Pharmacol. Exp-Therap. 102:* 1, 1951.
337. Hokin, L. E. and Hokin, M. R.: *Biochem. Biophys. Acta. 18:*102, 1955.
338. Fainschmidt, O.: *Biokhimiya. 1:*450, 1936.
339. Davidson, C. E. and Eiseman, B.: *Consciousness and the Chemical Environment of the Brain.* Report of the 25th Ross Pediatric Research Conf., 1957.
340. Schreiner, G.: *Consciousness and the Chemical Environment of the Brain.* Report of the 25th Ross Pediatric Conf., 1957, p. 60.
341. Waelsch, H., Sperry, W. M. and Stoyanoff, V. A.: *J. Biol. Chem. 135:*291, 1940.
342. Rossiter, R. J.: *Metabolism of the Nervous System.* Edited by Richter, D. New York, Pergamon Press, 1957, p. 355.
343. Gidez, L. I. and Karnovsky, M. L.: *J. Biol. Chem. 206:*229, 1954.
344. Pritchard, E. T.: *Fed. Proc. 15:*330, 1956.
345. Stetten, De W.: *J. Biol. Chem. 140:*143, 1941.
346. Fries, B. A., Schachner, H. and Chaikoff, I. L.: *J. Biol. Chem. 144:*59, 1942; *146:*95, 1942.
347. Naka, S.: *Metabolism of the Nervous System.* Edited by Richter, D. New York, Pergamon Press, 1957, p. 297.
348. Strickland, K. P.: *Canad. J. Biochem. Physiol. 32:*50, 1954.
349. Findlay, M., Strickland, K. P. and Rossiter, J. P.: *Canad. J. Biochem. Physiol. 32:*504, 1954.
350. Kennedy, E. P.: *Canad. J. Biochem. Physiol. 34:*334, 1956.
351. Berry, J. F. and McMurray, W. C.: *Canad. J. Biochem. Physiol. 35:*799, 1957.

352. Magee, W. L.: quoted in 342.
353. Hokin, L. E. and Hokin, M. R.: *Canad. J. Biochem. Physiol. 34:* 349, 1956.
354. Kornberg, A. and Pricer, W. E.: *J. Biol. Chem. 204:*345, 1953.
    Weiss, S. B., Smith, S. W. and Kennedy, E. P.: *Nature. 178:* 594, 1956.
    Weiss, S. B. and Kennedy, E. P.: *J. A. Chem. Soc. 78:*3550, 1956.
355. Brady, R. O., Formica, J. V. and Koval, G. J.: *J. Biol. Chem. 233:*1072, 1958.
    Brady, R. O. and Koval, G. J.: *J. Biol. Chem. 233:*26, 1958.
356. Cleland, W. W. and Kennedy, E. P.: *Fed. Proc. 17:*202, 1958.
357. Burton, R. M., Sodd, M. A. and Brady, R. O.: *Biochemistry of the Central Nervous System.* Proc. 4th Inter. Cong. Biochem. Vienna. Edited by Brucke, F. New York, Pergamon Press, 1959, p. 202.
358. Bogoch, S.: *Ibid.* p. 196, 1959.
359. Klenk, E.: *Biochemistry of the Developing Nervous System.* Edited by Waelsch, H. New York, Academic Press, 1955, p. 397.
    Penrose, L. S.: *Neurochemistry.* Edited by Elliott, K. A. C., Page, I. H. and Quastel, J. H. Springfield, Illinois, Charles C Thomas, 1955, p. 807.
    Jervis, G. A.: Effects of pharmacological agents on the nervous System, *Research Publ. A. Nerv. and Ment. Dis. 37:*162, 1959.
360. Offenstein, B., Schmidt, G. and Thannhauser, S. J.: *Blood. 3:* 1250, 1948.
361. Klenk, E.: *Ztschr. Physiol. Chem. 267:*128, 1940.
    Klenk, E., Rennkamp, F.: *Ztschr. Physiol. Chem. 272:*280, 1942.
362. Slome, D.: *J. Genetics. 27:*363, 1933.
363. Kalckar, H. M., Anderson, E. P. and Isselbacher, K. T.: *Proc. Nat. Acad. Sc. U.S. 42:*49, 1956. *Biochem. Biophys. Acta. 20:*262, 1956.
    Isselbacher, K. J., Anderson, E. P., Kurdhaski, K. and Kalckar, H. M.: *Science. 123:*635, 1956.
364. Sidbury, J. B.: *J. Clin. Invest. 36:*929, 1957.
365. Geiger, A.: *Metabolism of the Nervous System.* Edited by Richter, D. New York, Pergamon Press, 1957, p. 248.
366. Editorial, *New England J. Med. 237:*713, 1948.
367. Rossiter, R. J.: *Neurochemistry.* Edited by Elliott, K. A. C., Page, I. H. and Quastel, J. H. Springfield, Illinois, Charles C Thomas, 1955, p. 696.
368. Hurst, E. W.: *Australian J. Exper. Biol. & Med. 20:*297, 1942.
    Hicks, S. P.: *Arch. Path. 49:*111, 1950.

369. Earl, C. J. and Thompson, R. H. S.: *Brit. J. Pharmacol.* 7:261, 683, 1952.

370. Bennets, H. W. and Beck, A. B.: *Bull. 147. Council for Sc. Ind. Res.,* Australia 1942.

Innes, I. R. M.: *Multiple Sclerosis and Demyelinating Diseases.* Baltimore, Williams and Wilkins, 1950, p. 75.

371. Gallagher, C. H., Judah, J. D. and Reis, K. R.: *Proc. Roy. Soc. London, B. 145:*134, 195, 1956.

372. Houssay, B. A., Mazzocco, P. and Negrette, J.: *Compt. rend. Soc. biol. 11:*823, 1922.

373. Morrison, L. R. and Zamecnik, P. C.: *Arch. Neurol. & Psychiat. 63:*376, 1950.

374. Petrushka, E., Quastel, J. H. and Scholefield, P. G.: *Canad. J. Biochem. Physiol. 37:*975, 989, 1959.

375. Braganca, B. M. and Quastel, J. H.: *Biochem. J. 53:*88, 1953.

376. Donaldson, K. O., Nason, A., Lehman, I. R. and Nickon, A.: *J. Biol. Chem. 233:*572, 1958.

377. Sanders, M., Akin, B. A. and Soret, M. G.: *Acta. neuroveg. 8:*362, 1954.

378. Johnson, A. C., McNabb, A. R. and Rossiter, R. J.: *Arch. Neurol. Psychiat. 64:*105, 1950; *Biochem. J. 45:*500, 1949.

379. Thorn, G. W. and Forshan, P. H.: *Recent Progress in Hormone Research. 4:*243, 1949.

380. Bergen, J. R., Hunt, C. A. and Hoagland, H.: *Am. J. Physiol. 175:* 327, 1953.

381. Hayano, M., Schiller, S. and Dorfman, R. I.: *Endocrinology. 46:* 387, 1950.

382. Selye, H.: *Proc. Soc. Exper. Biol. & Med. 46:*116, 1941.

383. Gordan, G. S. and Elliott, H. W.: *Endocrinology. 41:*517, 1947.

Eisenberg, E., Gordan, G. S., Elliott, H. W. and Talbot, J.: *Proc. Soc. Exper. Biol. & Med. 73:*140, 1950.

384. Hoagland, H.: *Consciousness and the Chemical Environment of the Brain.* Report of the 25th Ross Pediatric Res. Conf., Ross Labs., 1957, p. 1.

385. Hoagland, H.: *Neurochemistry.* Edited by Elliott, K. A. C., Page, I. H. and Quastel, J. H. Springfield, Illinois, Charles C Thomas, 1955, p. 756.

386. Hochster, R. M. and Quastel, J. H.: *Nature. 164:*865, 1949; *Ann. N. Y. Acad. Sc. 54:*626, 1951.

387. Talalay, P. and Williams-Ashman, H. G.: *Proc. U.S. Nat. Acad. Sci. 44:*15, 1958.

Talalay, P., Hurlock, B. and Williams-Ashman, H. C.: *ibid. 44:*862, 1958.

Villee, C. A. and Hagerman, D. D.: *J. Biol. Chem. 233:*42, 1958.

388. Williams-Ashman, H. G., Cassman, M. and Klavins, M.: *Nature. 184:*42ı, 1959.

389. Gordan, G. S., Bentnick, R. C. and Eisenberg, E.: *Ann. N. Y. Acad. Sc. 54:*575, 1951.

390. Quastel, J. H. and Wheatley, A. H. M.: *Proc. Roy. Soc. London, B. 112:*60, 1932.

391. Quastel, J. H.: *Proc. Third Intern. Congress Biochemistry, Brussels,* 1955, p. 496.

392. Ghosh, J. J. and Quastel, J. H.: *Nature. 174:*28, 1954.

393. McIlwain, H.: *Biochem. J. 53:*403, 1953.

394. Brody, T. M. and Bain, J. A.: *Proc. Soc. Exper. Biol. & Med. 77:* 50, 1951.

395. Zeller, E. A.: *Pharmacol. Rev. 11:*387, 1959.

396. Shaw, J. L., Steele, B. F. and Lamb, C. A.: *Arch. Surg. 35:*1, 1937.

397. Dameshek, W., Myerson, A. and Loman, J.: *Amer. J. Psychiat. 91:* 113, 1934.

398. Michaelis, M. and Quastel, J. H.: *Biochem. J. 35:*918, 1941.

399. Edwards, C. and Larrabee, M. G.: *Fed. Proc. 12:*37, 1953.

400. Greig, M. E.: *J. Pharmacol. Exper. Therap. 91:*317, 1947.
   Rosenberg, A. J., Buchel, L., Etling, N. and Levi, J.: *Compt. rend. Soc. biol. 230:*480, 1950.
   Webb, J. L. and Elliott, K. A. C.: *J. Pharmacol. Exper. Therap. 103:*24, 1951.

401. Ernster, L., Low, H. and Lindberg, O.: *Acta. chem. scand. 9:*200, 1955.
   Ernster, L., Jalling, O., Low, H. and Lindberg, O.: *Exper. Cell. Res. Supp. 3:*124, 1955.

402. Mann, P. J. G., Tennenbaum, M. and Quastel, J. H.: *Biochem. J. 32:*243, 1938.
   Johnson, W. J. and Quastel, J. H.: *Nature. 171:*602, 1953.
   McLennan, H. and Elliott, K. A. C.: *J. Pharmacol Exper. & Ther. 103:*35, 1951.

403. Findlay, M., Strickland, K. P. and Rossiter, R. J.: *Canad. J. Biochem. Biophys. 32:*504, 1954.

404. Lewis, J. L. and McIlwain, H.: *Biochem. J. 57:*680, 1954.

405. McIlwain, H. and Greengard, O.: *J. Neurochem. 1:*348, 1957.

406. Magee, W. L., Berry, J. F. and Rossiter, R. J.: *Biochem. Biophys. Acta. 21:*408, 1956.

407. Jensen, P. K.: *Nature. 184:* Supp. 7, p. 451, 1959.

408. Bain, J. A.: *Progress in Neurobiology.* Edited by Waelsch, H. New York, Hoeber, 1957, 2:139.

409. Himwich, H. E., Sykowski, P. and Fazekas, J. F.: *Am. J. Physiol.* *132:*640, 1941.

410. Beer, C. T. and Quastel, J. H.: *Canad. J. Biochem. Physiol.* *36:* 543, 531, 1958.

411. Fischer, E.: *Alcoholism* (AAAS), 1957, p. 19.

412. Jacobs, P. A., Baiku, A. G., Court Brown, W. M. and Strong, J. A.: *Lancet 1:*710, 1959.

413. Sutherland, V. C., Hine, C. H. and Burbridge, T. N.: *J. Pharmacol. Exper. & Ther. 116:*469, 1956.

414. Wolpert, A., Truitt, E. B., Bell, F. K. and Krantz, J. L.: *J. Pharmacol. & Exper. Ther. 117:*358, 1956.

415. Berger, M., Strecker, H. J. and Waelsch, H.: *Nature. 177:*1234, 1956. *Ann. N. Y. Acad. Sc. 66:*806, 1957.

416. Zetterstrom, R. and Ernster, L.: *Nature. 178:*1335, 1957.

417. Axelrod, J., Schmid, R. and Hammaker, L.: *Nature. 180:*1426, 1957.

418. Gorten, M. K.: *Consciousness and the Chemical Environment of the Brain.* Report of the 25th Ross Pediatric Res. Conf., 1957, p. 108.

419. Thudichum, J. W. L.: *A Treatise on the Chemical Constitution of the Brain.* London, Balliére, Tindall and Cox, 1884.

420. Leake, C. D.: *Texas Rep. Biol. & Med. 13:*793, 1955.
Wooley, D. W. and Shaw, E. M.: *Ann. N. Y. Acad. Sc. 66:*649, 1957.
Marrazzi, A. S.: *Ann. N. Y. Acad. Sc. 66:*496, 1957.
Bain, J. A.: *Ann. N. Y. Acad. Sc. 66:*459, 1957.
Hoagland, H.: *Ann. N. Y. Acad. Sc. 66:*445, 1957; *J. Nerv. & Ment. Dis. 126:*211, 1958.

421. McFarland, R. A. and Goldstein, H.: *Am. J. Psychiatry. 95:*509, 1938.
Richter, D.: Biochemical aspects of schizophrenia in *Schizophrenia; Somatic Aspects.* New York, Pergamon Press, 1957, p. 53.
Horwitt, M. K.: *Science. 124:*429, 1956.
Evarts, E. V.: *Psychiat. Res. Report. 9:*52, 1958.
McDonald, R. K.: *J. Chronic Diseases. 8:*366, 1958.

422. Kety, S. S.: *Science. 129:*1528, 1959.

423. Himwich, H. E.: *Science. 127:*59, 1958.

424. Kleist, K.: *Klin. Wchnschr. 2:*962, 1923.

425. Gjessing, R.: *Arch. Psychiat. Nervenke. 96:*319, 1932.
Gjessing, R.: *J. Mental Sc. 84:*608, 1938.
Gjessing, L., Bernhardser, A. and Froshaug, J: *J. Mental Sc. 104:*188, 1958.

426. Quastel, J. H. and Wales, W. T.: *Lancet. ii:*301, 1938; *i:*402, 1940.

427. Basowitz, H., Persky, H., Korchin, S. J. and Grinker, R. G.: *Anxiety and Stress.* Chicago, McGraw Hill, 1955.

428. Georgyi, A., Fischer, R., Weber, R. and Weiss, P.: *Schweiz. Med. Wchnschr.* 78:1194, 1948.
429. Buscaino, V. M.: *Acta Neurol.* (Naples). 13:1, 1958.
430. McGeer, P. L., McNair, F. E., McGeer, E. G., Gibson, W. C.: *J. Nerv. & Ment. Dis.* 125:166, 1957.
431. Georgi, F., Honegger, C. G., Jordan, D., Rieder, H. P. and Rotten-berg, M.: *Klin. Wchnschr.* 34:799, 1956.
     Riegelhaupt, L. M.: *J. Nerv. & Ment. Dis.* 123:383, 1956.
     Cafruny, E. J. and Domino, E. F.: *Arch. Neurol. Psychiat.* 79: 336, 1958.
432. Acheson, R. M., Paul, R. M. and Tomlinson, R. V.: *Canad. J. Biochem. Physiol.* 36:295, 1958.
433. Amine oxidase inhibitors. *Ann. N. Y. Acad. Sc.* 80:551, 772, 1959.
434. Bogdanski, D. F., Weissbach, H. and Udenfriend, S.: *J. Neurochem.* 1:272, 1957.
     Paasonen, P. D., MacLean, P. D. and Giarman, N. J.: *ibid.* 1: 326, 1957.
435. Shore, P. A., Pletscher, A., Tomich, E. G., Carlsson, A., Kuntz-man, R. and Brodie, B. B.: *Ann. N. Y. Acad. Sc.* 66:609, 1957.
436. Udenfriend, S., Weissbach, H. and Bogdanski, D. F.: *Ann. N. Y. Acad. Sc.* 66:602, 1957.
437. Symposium on catecholamines. *Pharmacol. Rev.* 11:233, 1959.
438. Rothballer, A. B.: *Pharmacol. Rev.* 11:494, 1959.
439. Millen, J. W. and Hess, A.: *Brain.* 81:248, 1958.
440. Coulter, V. A.: *Am. J. Physiol.* 195:459, 1958.
441. Edstrom, R.: *Acta psych neurol. scand.* 33:403, 1958.
442. Van Harreveld, A. and Schade, J. P.: Abstr. International Meeting Neurobiol. Amsterdam, 1959, p. 32.
443. Eccles, J. C.: *The Physiology of Nerve Cells.* Baltimore, Johns Hopkins Press, 1957.
444. Ussing, H. H.: *Biochemistry of the Central Nervous System.* Symposium. Proc. 4th Inter. Cong. Biochem. Vienna. Edited by Brucke, F. New York, Pergamon Press, 1959, p. 1.
445. Teorell, T.: *Exper. Cell. Res. Supp.* 5, 1958, p. 83.
446. Hodgkin, A. L.: *Biol. Rev.* 26:339, 1951.
447. Godwin, J. T., Farr, L. E., Sweet, W. H. and Robertson, J. C.: *Cancer.* 8:601, 1955.
     Slatkin, D. N.: *McGill Medical Journal.* 27:20, 1958.
448. Henderson, W.: *Arch. Dis. Childhood.* 33:114, 1958.
449. Southren, A. L., Warner, R. R. P., Christoff, N. I. and Weiner, H. E.: *New England J. Med.* 260:1265, 1959.

450. Penrose, L. S.: Medical Research Council Special Report No. 229., *A Clinical and Genetic Study of 1280 Cases of Mental Defect.* London, H. M. Stationery Office, 1938.

451. Himwich, H. E. and Fazekas, J. F.: *Arch. Neurol. Psychiat. 44:* 1213, 1940; *51:*73, 1944.

452. Benda, C. E.: *Am. J. Ment. Def. 45:*42, 1940.

453. Stanburg, J. B. and Hedge, A. N.: *J. Clin. Endocrinol. 10:*1471. 1950.

454. Stanburg, J. B., Ohela, K. and Pitt-Rivers, R.: *J. Clin. Endocrinol. 15:*54, 1955.

455. Penrose, L. S.: *Biochemistry of the Developing Nervous System.* Edited by Waelsch, H. New York, Academic Press, 1955, p. 411.

456. Dawkins, M. J. R., Judah, J. D. and Rees, K. R.: *Biochem. J. 73:*16, 1959.

457. Von Muralt, A.: *Exper. Cell. Research, Supp. 5. 72:*1958.

458. Hsia, D. Y. Y., Driscoll, K., Troll, W. and Knox, W. E.: *Nature. 178:*1279, 1956.

459. Goldbloom, A. and Brickman, H. F.: *J. Pediat. 28:*674, 1946.

460. Dormandy, T. L., Leak, D. and Grant H.: *Lancet* vol. *2:* p. 269, 1959.

461. Geren, B. B.: *Exper. Cell. Research. 7:*558, 1954.

462. Hoeffer, P. F. and Glaser, G. H.: *J.A.M.A. 143:*620, 1950.

463. Henser, Y.: *Rev. Canad. Biol. 17:*229, 1958.

464. Blanc, W. A. and Johnson, L.: *J. Neuropath and Exp. Neur. 18:* 165, 1959.

465. Odell, G. B.: *J. Pediat. 55:*268, 1959.

466. Walshe, J. M.: *Brit. Med. Bull. 13:*132, 1957.

467. Mackenzie, D. Y. and Woolf, C. I.: *Brit. M. J. 1:*90, 1959.

468. de Robertis, E.: *Experimental Cell Research Suppl. 5:*347, 1958.

469. Bessman, S. P., Merlis, J. K. and Borges, F.: *Proc. Soc. Exper. Biol. & Med. 95:*502, 1957.

470. Conn, H. O.: *New England J. Med. 259:*564, 1958.

471. Goldberg, A.: *Quart. J. Med. 28:*183, 1959.

472. Williams, J. V., Jr., Monson, W. J., Harper, A. E., and Elvehjem, C. A.: *J. Biol. Chem. 202:*600, 1953.

473. Heald, P. J.: *Biochem. J. 73:*132, 1959.

474. Dancis, J. and Balis, M. E.: *Pediatrics. 15:*63, 1955.

475. Kini, M. M. and Quastel, J. H.: *Science. 131:*412, 1960.

476. Wollenberger, A.: *Biochem. J. 61:*68, 77, 1955.

477. Shanes, A. M.: *Pharmacol. Rev. 10:*59, 165, 1958.

478. Welsh, J. H. and Gordon, H. T.: *J. Cell. Comp. Physiol. 30:*147, 1947; *31:*395, 1948.

479. Shanes, A. M.: *Ann. N. Y. Acad. Sc. 55:*1, 1952.

480. Shanes, A. M., Grundfest, H. and Freygang, W.: *J. Gen. Physiol.* *37:*39, 1953.
481. Gershfeld, N. L. and Shanes, A. M.: *Science.* *129:*1427, 1959.
482. Straub, R.: *Helv. Physiol. Pharmacol. Acta.* *14:*1, 1956.
483. Koch, J. H. and Gallagher, C. H.: *Nature.* *184:*1039, 1959.
484. Banister, J., Whittaker, V. P. and Wijesunderas: *J. Physiol. 121:* 55, 1953.
    Henschler, D.: *Naturwiss. 43:*522, 1956.
485. Holtz, P. and Schuemann, H. J.: *Naturwiss. 41:*306, 1954.
486. Gruner, G. and Kewitz, H.: *Naturwiss. 42:*628, 1955.
487. Keyl, M. J., Michaelson, I. A. and Whittaker, V. P.: *J. Physiol. 139:*434, 1957.
    Whittaker, V. P.: *Biochem. J. 71:*32, 1959.
    Erspamer, V. and Glaesser, A.: *Brit. J. Pharmacol. 12:*176, 1957.
488. Berry, J. F. and Whittaker, V. P.: *Biochem. J. 73:*447, 1959.
489. Burgen, A. S. V., Burke, G. and Desbarats-Schonbaum, M.: *Brit. J. Pharmacol. 11:*308, 1956.
490. Dawkins, M. J. R., Judah, J. D. and Rees, K. R.: *Biochem. J. 72:* 204; *73:*16, 1959.
491. Feldberg, W. and Fleischhauer, K.: *J. Physiol. 150:*451, 1960.
492. Allweis, C. and Magnes, J.: *J. Neurochem. 2:*326, 1958.
493. Stevenson, I. and Sanchez, A. J.: *Amer. J. Psychiat. 114:*328, 1957.
494. Stevenson, I. and Mokrasch, L. C.: *Amer. J. Psychiat. 114:*1038, 1958.
495. Delay, J., Gerard, H. P. and Thullier, J.: *Compt. Rend. Soc. Biol. 144:*163, 1950.
496. Wallgren, H. and Kulonen, E.: *Biochem. J. 75:*150, 1960.
497. Desbarats-Schonbaum, M. L. and Birmingham, M. K.: *J. Gerontology 14:* 284, 1959.
498. Balazs, R. and Lagnado, J. R.: *J. Neurochem. 5:*1, 1959.
499. Wu, R. and Racker, E.: *J. Biol. Chem. 234:*1029, 1959.
500. McCaman, R. E. and Robins, E.: *J. Neurochem. 5:*18, 32, 1959.
501. Brante, G.: *Acta physiol. scand. 18:*Suppl. 63, 1, 1949.
502. Hollinger, D. M. and Rossiter, R. J.: *Biochem. J. 52:*659, 1952.
    Hollinger D. M., Rossiter, R. J. and Upmalis, H.: *Biochem. J. 52:* 652, 1952.
503. Del Castillo, J. and Katz, B.: *Progress in Biophysics and Biophysical Chemistry. 6:*121, 1956.
504. Price, S. A. P. and West, G. B.: *Nature 185:*470, 1960.
505. Berry, J. F. and McMurray, W. C.: *Canad. J. Biochem. Physiol. 35:* 799, 1957.
506. Mills, C. F. and Fell, B. F.: *Nature. 185:*20, 1960.
507. Ashwood-Smith, M. J. and Smith, A. D.: *Nature. 184:*2028, 1959.

508. Hokin, L. E. and Hokin, M. R.: *Nature. 184:*Suppl. 14, 1068, 1959.
509. Solomon, A., Lionetti, F. and Curran, P.: *Nature. 178:*582, 1956.
     Vogt, M.: *Nature. 179:*300, 1957.
     Kirshner, L. B.: *J. Gen. Physiol. 42:*231, 1958.
510. Porter, H. and Ainsworth, S.: *J. Neurochem. 5:*91, 1959.
511. Brodie, B. B. and Shore, P. A.: *Ann. N. Y. Acad. Sc. 66:*631, 1957.
512. Canal, N. and Maffer-Faccioli, A.: *J. Neurochem. 5:*99, 1959.
513. Peters, E. L. and Tower, D. B.: *J. Neurochem. 5:*80, 1959.
514. Axelrod, J., Albers, W. and Clemente, C. D.: *J. Neurochem. 5:*68, 1959.
515. Giuditta, A. and Strecker, H. J.: *J. Neurochem. 5:*50, 1959.
516. Kaplan, N. O., Colowick, S. P. and Neufeld, F.: *J. Biol. Chem. 205:*1, 1953.
517. Sporn, M. B., Dingman, W., Defalco, A. and Davies, R. K.: *J. Neurochem. 5:*62, 1959.
518. Elliott, K. A. C. and Van Gelder, N. B.: *J. Neurochem. 3:*28, 1958.
519. Cumings, J. N.: *Biochemical Aspects of Neurological Disorders.* Ed.: J. N. Cumings and M. Kremer. Springfield, Illinois, Charles C Thomas, 1959, p. 98.
520. Hurst, E. W.: *Aust. J. Exp. Biol. Med. Sc. 20:*297, 1942.
521. Rimington, C.: as in 519, p. 57.
522. Spillane, J. D.: *loc. cit.,* p. 10.
523. Quastel, J. H.: Biochemistry of the Central Nervous System. Symposium. *Fourth International Congress of Biochem. Vienna 3:*90, 1959. Ed.: Brucke, F. Pergamon Press.
524. Sved, S.: Ph.D. Thesis. McGill University, 1958.

INDEX